3–6 Overhead Manipulatives

in Action

Barbara Bando Irvin

Table of Contents

Overhead and Classroom Manipulatives

All of the overhead manipulatives used in the activities in this book and suggested classroom manipulatives are available from Learning Resources. The overhead manipulatives are listed in *italic*.

Required Materials

Base Ten Blocks
LER 650 Overhead Base Ten Blocks
LER 630 Base Ten Block Transparencies
LER 930 Plastic Base Ten Starter Set or
LER 231 Wood Base Ten Starter Set
LER 924–927 Plastic Base Ten Components
LER 124–127 Wood Base Ten Components

Hundred Board
LER 475 Overhead Hundred Grid
LER 375 Hundred Boards
LER 131 Transparent Counters

Bills and Coins
LER 625   Overhead Coin Set
LER 635   Overhead Bills
LER 101   Coin Set or
LER 95–99 Coins in bulk
LER 104   Paper Money in Wallet Set or
LER 91–94 Paper Money in bulk

Pattern Blocks
LER 640 Overhead Pattern Blocks
LER 134 Plastic Pattern Blocks or
LER 334 Wooden Pattern Blocks

Geoboards
LER 152T Transparent Geoboard
LER 152   Plastic Geoboard

Fraction Squares
LER 251 Overhead Fraction Squares

Tangrams
LER 418 Tangrams for the Overhead
LER 417 Tangrams

Rainbow Fraction Tiles
LER 616 Overhead Rainbow Fraction Tiles
LER 615 Rainbow Fraction Tiles

Transparent Grids
LER 309 Inch Grids 10" × 10"
LER 310 Centimeter Grids 25 × 25 cm
LER 311 Mini Metric Grids 10 × 10 cm

Additional Materials

LER 128   Base Ten Block Stamps
LER 230   Base Ten Block Activity Book
LER 130A Base Ten Block Activity Set
LER 130B Base Ten Place Value Charts

LER 377 1–100 Activity Book
LER 376 1–100 Demo Kit
LER 1330 Hundred Number Board
LER 378 Overhead Numbers, 1–100
LER 381 Number Squares 1–100
LER 203 Square Color Tiles

LER 102 Coin Stamps—Heads
LER 103 Coin Stamps—Tails
LER 80 Magnetic Money
LER 81 Fun With Money Activity Book
LER 85 Currency-X-Change
LER 105 Money Activity Book
LER 106 Classroom Money Kit with Tray
LER 107 Coin Matching Cards
LER 108 Making Change Cards (to $1.00)
LER 109 Making Change Cards (to $10.00)
LER 202 Coin Cube
LER 2628 Calculator Cash Register

LER 1391 Pattern Block Template
LER 267 Pattern Block Rubber Stamps
LER 264 Pattern Block Activity Cards
LER 268 Pattern Block Stickers
LER 330 Pattern Block Party
LER 335 Pattern Block Activity Pack
LER 336 Patternables
LER 337 Pattern Block Work Tray
LER 350 Marvelous Mosaics Set

LER 421 Primary Geoboard Activity Book
LER 422 Intermediate Geoboard Activity Book
LER 915 Transparent Geoboard 10" × 10"

LER 115 Circular Fraction Set
LER 116 Square Fraction Set
LER 250 Fraction Activity Flash Cards

LER 118 Tangram Kit
LER 318 Tangramables
LER 519 Tangrams in Action Binder

Introduction and Use

Overhead Manipulatives in Action, 3–6 is a collection of 40 lessons designed to help teachers make the best use of eight different manipulatives on the overhead projector. The lessons have been carefully developed to present explorations and demonstrations with concrete models. Engaging students in explorations—learning by doing, thinking, and talking—not only improves mathematics skills, but also visual perception, memory, and critical thinking skills. Problem-solving strategies, and communication and socialization skills will also be greatly enhanced.

This teacher resource book is organized into eight sections focusing on the following overhead manipulatives:

- Base Ten Blocks
- Hundred Boards
- Bills and Coins
- Pattern Blocks
- Geoboards
- Fraction Squares
- Tangrams
- Rainbow Fraction Tiles

Some lessons also feature activities with Transparent Counters and Transparent Grids.

The lessons in *Overhead Manipulatives in Action, 3–6* cover a wide range of mathematical topics and practical skills that can be integrated into any existing mathematics curriculum, grades 3 through 6. They include:

- sorting
- classifying
- counting
- comparing
- patterns
- sequences
- place value
- numeration
- addition
- subtraction
- multiplication
- division
- shape identification
- congruence
- similarity
- symmetry
- counting money
- making change
- fractions
- decimals
- percent
- fraction operations
- estimation
- mental computation

The activities build sequentially on students' prior learning to ensure a logical progression of skill development and to make the connection between different mathematical topics. Refer to the Table of Contents to find a specific topic and integrate it into your mathematics curriculum.

NCTM Standards

The lessons in this book were developed using the NCTM's *Curriculum and Evaluation Standards for School Mathematics* (1989) as a guideline. Through these lessons, students will become actively involved in developing mathematics understanding and relationships. By incorporating the first four process-oriented standards throughout this program for any mathematical topic, students will be better able to solve problems, apply reasoning abilities, make connections, and communicate ideas.

The activities provided afford various opportunities for using problem-solving strategies such as making lists, drawing pictures, using the process of elimination, and writing an equation for a problem. Emphasis is placed on reasoning and critical thinking skills as students are asked what they think about a problem, how many possible ways they can find to solve a problem, or whether they can justify their answers. By questioning, discussing, showing and telling, and writing short descriptions to share ideas with classmates, students acquire the language and concepts of mathematics. Since it is important that students connect ideas both among and within areas of mathematics, some of the topics in this program will use more than one type of overhead manipulative.

Using *Overhead Manipulatives in Action, 3–6*

Overhead Manipulatives in Action, 3–6 consists of eight sections of five lessons each. In addition to the 40 lessons, teaching suggestions are included at the beginning, and several forms (Student Progress Chart, Family Letter, and Certificates) are included at the back of this book to facilitate classroom management and communication.

Each section begins with an overview of the content, lists of materials needed, and a *Getting Started* activity, followed by three or five pages of overhead manipulatives that may be duplicated for student use.

 ## The Lesson Plan

Each lesson consists of a page of teaching notes and an overhead blackline master. Teaching notes contain the following information and types of activities:

Objective	The goal of the lesson.
Vocabulary	A list of mathematical terms to focus on the language of mathematics.
Materials	A list of materials is given to help you prepare for your presentation and for student activities.
Warm-Up	Tasks to review necessary prerequisite skills or to set the stage for the lesson.
Activity	Step-by-step directions to ensure well-planned demonstrations and explorations for a specific math objective. Set-up procedures, suggested questions, and even some sample scripts are included.
Practice	Suggestions to enable students to work individually, in pairs, or in small cooperative groups to complete an activity.
Wrap-Up	Summarizes the lesson and checks students' understanding.

Some lessons contain an Extension Activity to provide additional challenge to students. Although many suggestions are provided to help you implement the lessons, only you can decide how to organize students and materials to suit your classroom needs.

You can use the overhead blackline masters to make an overhead transparency or a student worksheet. It is essential that you duplicate copies of the blackline master for students when you are working with the transparency on the projector so that they can actively participate. Several of the overhead blackline masters are generic enough to be used with other overhead manipulative lessons or with other curriculum topics. For example, the Hundred Board on page 22, One Hundred Squares on page 23, Dot Paper on page 68, the One and Hundredths grids on page 80, and Inch and Centimeter Grids on pages 95 and 96 can be used over and over with many lessons.

Using the Overhead Projector

Using manipulatives on the overhead projector will help you become a more effective educator. Your demonstrations will become more colorful and filled with movement. Also, by facing students, you will be able to maintain eye contact with them as well as to observe whether they are on task. Several student response techniques may be employed besides calling out answers or raising hands; students can hold up cards for you to see and no one else, indicate thumbs-up, thumbs-down responses, or use air writing. Whichever response technique you use, be sure to inform students about it before the lesson begins.

Each lesson lists the materials needed to carry out the activity. However, here is a list of materials you should have available for every lesson:
- ◆ Set of erasable overhead color pens
- ◆ Blank transparencies
- ◆ Sheets of blank paper or light weight tagboard
- ◆ Spray bottle of water
- ◆ Paper towel or cloth
- ◆ Extra overhead projector bulb

Having a blank transparency placed over the overhead master transparency will allow you to move or remove all the manipulative pieces at one time or to draw lines or write answers without messing up the original. Use sheets of paper to play "cover-up" games, "flash" games, or to expose only portions of a transparency at a time.

To facilitate lesson presentations, arrange the overhead manipulatives on a piece of acetate or tagboard and place it near the projector. For example, having all the Pattern Blocks sorted and in sight will help you find the blocks quickly as you model a mathematical situation.

You may wish to purchase plastic ziplock pockets for the three-ring binders so that you can store a set of each overhead manipulative with each section of lessons in this binder.

 # Student Materials

Besides having the appropriate classroom manipulatives available, the following materials should also be handy to enable the students to complete the activities:
- ◆ Sheets of blank paper
- ◆ Spiral theme book or tablet
- ◆ Set of crayons or color markers
- ◆ Pencils with erasers
- ◆ Scissors
- ◆ Paste, glue, or tape
- ◆ Pocket envelopes or plastic ziplock bags

You may also wish to permit students to have basic four-function calculators to help them find multiple solutions to some problems or to verify their estimates or solutions.

Encourage students to make their own sets of manipulatives and store them in envelopes or plastic bags. They will get into the habit of using materials to understand problems and to find solutions. Also, make some of the manipulatives available at all times so students can use their leisure time to create patterns or invent new problems.

Class Management

Depending on the availability of classroom manipulatives and ability levels, students can work individually, in pairs, in small cooperative groups, or as an entire class. Some activities are more conducive than others for working together.

To keep track of a student's progress, a Student Progress Chart is provided. A generic Family Letter allows you to suggest how family members can help students learn more about a mathematical concept or skill. For students needing more tangible means of encouragement or recognition, three types of certificates are provided.

Base Ten Blocks

Introduction

Base Ten Blocks are an excellent hands-on manipulative for learning about place value concepts and operations with whole numbers. The focus in grades 3 through 6 will be on place value of three- and four-digit numbers and understanding the operations of addition, subtraction, multiplication, and division using one-, two-, three-, and four-digit numbers.

Base Ten Block Activities

 Getting Organized

Materials you will need:
- ◆ *Base Ten Block Transparencies* (LER 630)
- ◆ *Overhead Base Ten Blocks* (LER 650)
- ◆ *Transparent Counters* (LER 131)
- ◆ One transparency each of pages 9, 10, 12, 14, 16, 18, 20
- ◆ Blank transparencies, overhead pens

When working with two-digit numbers, you may wish to use the two-dimensional set of blocks (*Overhead Base Ten Blocks*) since they are larger and easier to handle on the projector.

Materials students will need:
- ◆ *Base Ten Blocks* (plastic or wood)
- ◆ Copies of pages 6, 7, 8, 9, 10, 12, 14, 16, 18, 20
- ◆ Scissors, pencils, paper

Duplicate pages 6, 7, and 8 on brightly colored paper as colorful base ten blocks will add more interest to the activities.

 Getting Started

By third grade most students will have been exposed to base ten blocks, especially the ones, tens, and hundreds blocks. Take a few minutes to talk about the blocks and ask them how they have used them before. Using the *Base Ten Transparencies* (LER 630), review the names and values of the ones, tens, and hundreds base ten blocks with students by displaying them on the projector one at a time. Introduce the thousands block at this time. Some students may refer to the **ones blocks** as *units*, the **tens blocks** as *longs* or *rods*, the **hundreds blocks** as *flats*, and the **thousands blocks** as *cubes*.

Next, review place value for two-digit numbers. Display a model for a two-digit number using the ones and tens blocks. Then ask students for the number it represents. For example, show 5 tens and 7 ones [57]. After students name the number, reverse the task by writing a two-digit number on the projector and asking students to use base ten blocks to model it.

To review comparison concepts, write 2 two-digit numbers on the projector and ask students to use their ones and tens blocks to show whether the two numbers are *equivalent to* or *more (less) than* each other. Include pairs of numbers such as 57 and 37, 35 and 35, and 26 and 62.

Ones and Tens

Overhead Manipulatives in Action, 3–6
© 1992 Learning Resources, Inc.

Hundreds

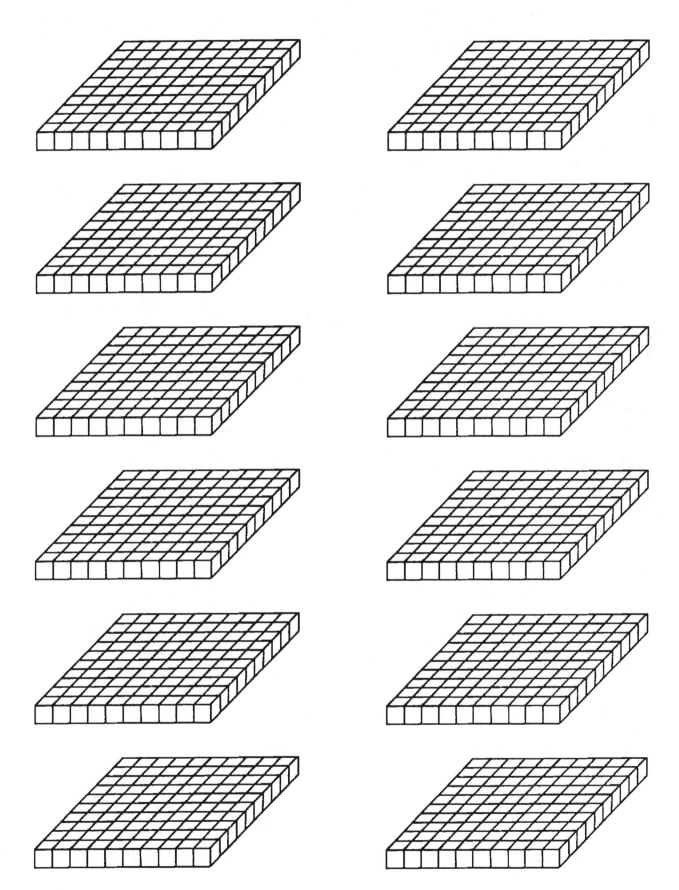

Thousands

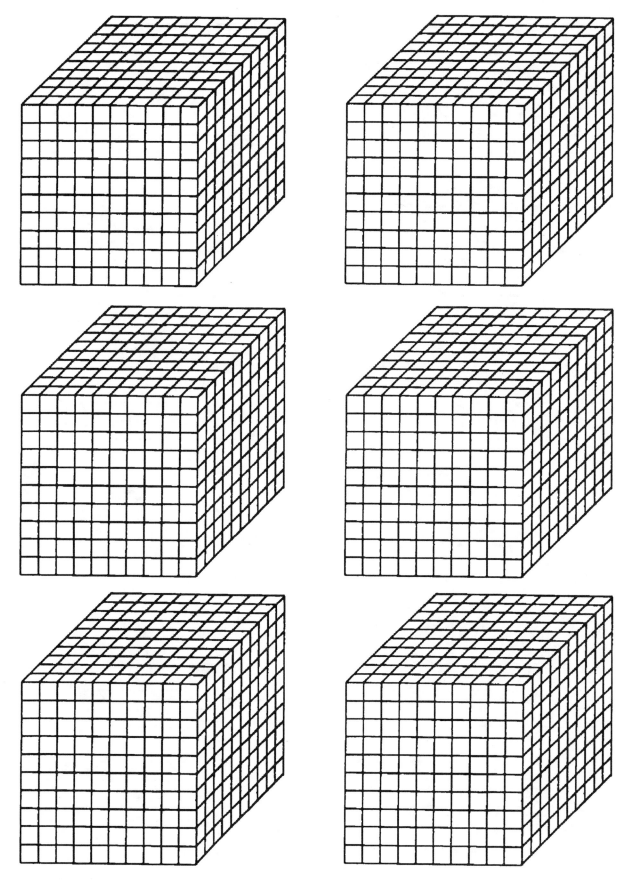

Overhead Manipulatives in Action, 3–6
© 1992 Learning Resources, Inc.

Place Value Mat

HUNDREDS	TENS	ONES

Overhead Manipulatives in Action, 3–6
© 1992 Learning Resources, Inc.

Base Ten Blocks

Place Value Mat

Thousands	Hundreds	Tens	Ones

Blocks and Numbers

 Objectives

To model a number using base ten blocks.
To determine the number for a given set of base ten blocks.
To write the number name for a given number or set of base ten blocks.

Vocabulary

ones, tens, hundreds, thousands, place value, number, numeral, number name

Materials

Base Ten Block Transparencies, transparency of page 12, blank transparencies, overhead pens; *Base Ten Blocks,* student copies of pages 6, 7, and 12, scissors, paste

Warm-Up

Have students review counting by tens to 100 and counting by hundreds to 1000. You may also wish to show a list of words for the teens and tens so that students will be able to write the number name for a given number in the activity that follows.

Activity

Blocks and Numbers. Display the transparency of page 12 on the projector and give students base ten blocks and two copies of page 12. Place the base ten blocks on the transparency to show the number 346. Direct students to show the same number of blocks on their place value chart. Ask:

How many ones are there? [6]
How many tens are there? [4]
How many hundreds are there? [3]
What is the number? [346]
Write the numeral in the box at the top of the page. [346]
How would you write the number name? [three hundred forty-six]
Write the number name on the lines shown.

Repeat the activity to include numbers like 420, 608, and 413. You can modify the activity two ways: write a three-digit number in the box at the top of the page and then have students show the correct number of blocks and write the number name; or write the number name and then have students write the numeral and show the correct number of blocks.

Practice

Write several three-digit numbers on the projector, such as 700, 456, 209, and 350. Ask students to choose one number and model it with base ten blocks by cutting and pasting blocks from pages 6 and 7. Then ask them to write the number name.

Wrap-Up

Have each student show and tell about the number shown on his or her sheet. Discuss the place value of the digits, especially the importance of zero.

Extension Activity

Let students identify and form four-digit numbers with their base ten blocks. Use the place value mat on page 10.

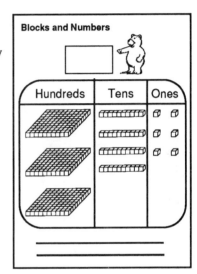

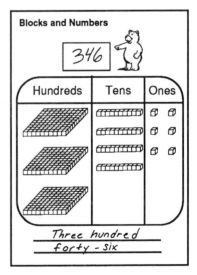

Blocks and Numbers

HUNDREDS	TENS	ONES

_____

_____

Understanding Addition

 ## Objective

To solve addition problems involving one-, two- and three-digit numbers using base ten blocks.

Vocabulary

add, addend, sum, regroup (trade), in all, altogether, total

Materials

Base Ten Block Transparencies, transparencies of pages 9 and 14, blank transparencies, overhead pens; *Base Ten Blocks, Base Ten Block Stamps,* student copies of page 14, pencils

Warm-Up

Review the basic facts for addition with students. Then review regrouping ones to tens (trading up). Give students base ten blocks and display the transparency of page 9 on the projector. To introduce regrouping tens and hundreds, place 2 hundreds and 14 tens on the transparency. Help students regroup the tens to hundreds, then name the number [340]. Repeat the activity including sets of base ten blocks that require two regroupings; for example, 2 hundreds, 11 tens, 15 ones [325].

Activity

Addition. Distribute base ten blocks and page 14. Write an addition exercise at the top of the page. Have students use their place value mats and base ten blocks to represent the addition exercise, then regroup to find the sum. Continue with other addition exercises involving regrouping.

Practice

Ask pairs of students to work as follows—one thinks of an addition problem and the other solves it using base ten blocks. Students can take turns for three rounds. They may create their own problems or refer to their textbook for sets of problems. Give students extra copies of page 14, cutouts (pages 6 and 7), and paste, or base ten block stamps, to record their problems.

Wrap-Up

Ask pairs of volunteers to show their problems and explain how they found the sums. Emphasize the language associated with addition as students give their explanations.

Extension Activity

Try addition problems using four-digit numbers. Use the place value mat on page 10.

Try these problems.

Without regrouping			With regrouping:			Column addition:		
326	403	170	237	375	276	234	318	302
+ 52	+ 235	+ 222	+ 115	+ 150	+ 147	172	50	6
[378]	[638]	[392]	[352]	[525]	[423]	+ 300	+ 132	+ 81
						[706]	[500]	[389]

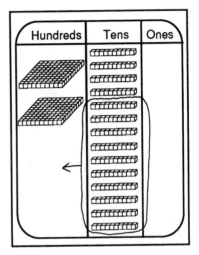

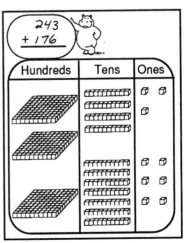

Base Ten Blocks

Addition

$$+ \underline{}$$

HUNDREDS	TENS	ONES

Overhead Manipulatives in Action, 3–6
© 1992 Learning Resources, Inc.

Understanding Subtraction

 Objective

To solve subtraction problems involving one-, two- and three-digit numbers using base ten blocks.

Vocabulary

subtract, difference, are left, regroup (trade)

Materials

Base Ten Block Transparencies, transparencies of pages 9 and 16, blank transparencies, overhead pens; *Base Ten Blocks, Base Ten Block Stamps*, student copies of page 16, pencils

Warm-Up

Review the basic subtraction facts and regrouping tens to ones (trading down) with students. Then introduce regrouping involving tens and hundreds. Display the transparency of page 9 on the projector and give base ten blocks to students. Show 2 hundreds and 4 tens on the transparency. Ask students to suggest ways they could show this number with more tens blocks in the tens column. [Trade 1 hundred for 10 tens.] Model this on the projector as students model it with their base ten blocks. Repeat the activity to include numbers like 400 [3 hundreds, 10 tens] and 315 [2 hundreds, 11 tens, 5 ones].

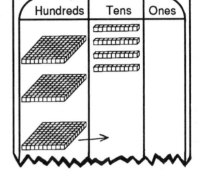

Activity

Subtraction. Distribute base ten blocks and page 16. Write a subtraction exercise at the top of the page. Have students copy it and use their base ten blocks to find the difference. Continue with other subtraction exercises including regrouping and no regrouping.

Practice

Direct students to work in pairs—one to think of a subtraction problem, the other to solve the problem using the base ten blocks. Have them take turns for at least three rounds. Students may create their own problems or refer to their textbook for sets of problems. Give students extra copies of page 16, cutouts (pages 6 and 7), and paste or base ten block stamps to record their problems.

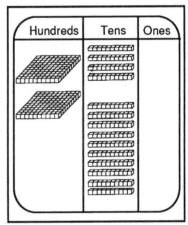

Wrap-Up

Ask pairs of volunteers to show their problems and to explain how they found the differences. Emphasize the language associated with subtraction as students give their explanations.

Extension Activity

Try subtraction problems using four-digit numbers and page 10. Some students may wish to practice their subtraction skills in a practical way by having them make change from a one-dollar or five-dollar bill for a purchase.

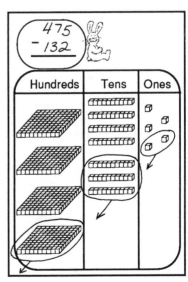

Try these problems.

Without regrouping:

549	482	185
−132	− 50	−102
[417]	[432]	[83]

With regrouping:

372	528	400
−145	−290	−123
[227]	[238]	[277]

Subtraction

HUNDREDS	TENS	ONES

Base Ten Blocks

(16)

Understanding Multiplication

 Objective

To solve multiplication problems with a one-digit multiplier using base ten blocks.

Vocabulary

multiply, factor, product, altogether, in all, repeated addition

Materials

Base Ten Block Transparencies, transparency of page 18, blank transparencies, overhead pens; *Base Ten Blocks*, student copies of page 18, pencils

Warm-Up

Review the basic facts for multiplication with students. You may wish to illustrate a few multiplication facts, such as 5×3. Extend knowledge of the basic facts to include practice with related facts such as 50×3 or 500×3.

Activity 1

Multiplication and Repeated Addition. Display the transparency of page 18 on the projector, then give students base ten blocks and page 18. Write the problem 23×5 at the top of the page. Ask, **If 7×5 is the same as five groups of seven or "$7 + 7 + 7 + 7 + 7$," what do you think 23×5 means?** Responses should include "five groups of 23" or "$23 + 23 + 23 + 23 + 23$." Write the addition problem $23 + 23 + 23 + 23 + 23$ next to the multiplication problem. Then ask the class how they would show five groups of 23. Show five groups of 23 on the projector with the base ten blocks. Students can use base ten blocks to model the problem with you as you add each group of 23—23, 46, 69, 92 (regroup tens and ones), 115 (regroup tens and hundreds). Try other problems such as 24×4 or 48×6 showing multiplication as repeated addition.

Activity 2

Multiplication Algorithm. Write the problem 23×5 at the top of the page. Show five groups of 23. Tell students to consider 23 as the quantity $20 + 3$, then multiply 20 and 3 each by 5. The partial products will yield the total number of the ones [$3 \times 5 = 15$ (regroup to 1 ten and 5 ones)] and the total number of tens [$20 \times 5 = 100$ (regroup 10 tens to 1 hundred)] to give the product 115 for the problem 23×5.

Practice

Let students work in pairs—one to think of a multiplication problem, the other to solve the problem using the base ten blocks. Have them take turns for at least three rounds.

Wrap-Up

Call on volunteers to show their problems and to explain how they found the products.

Extension Activity

Let students use play money to show how to solve multiplication problems. Students can use page 48 with this activity.

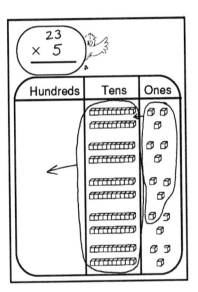

Try these problems:

23	45	34
× 3	× 2	× 8
[69]	[90]	[272]

219	135	204
× 4	× 6	× 3
[876]	[810]	[612]

Multiplication

$$\times \,\underline{}$$

HUNDREDS	TENS	ONES

Overhead Manipulatives in Action, 3–6
© 1992 Learning Resources, Inc.

Understanding Division

Objective

To solve a division problem with a one-digit divisor using base ten blocks.

Vocabulary

divide, divisor, dividend, quotient, remainder

Materials

Base Ten Block Transparencies, Transparent Counters, transparency of page 20, blank transparencies, overhead pens; *Base Ten Blocks*, student copies of page 20, pencils

Warm-Up

Review the basic facts for division with students. You may wish to illustrate a few division facts, such as $18 \div 3$. Display a set of 18 counters and then divide them into three groups to find how many counters are in each group. *Note:* Due to the limited space on page 20, use only divisors 2, 3, and 4 to show the concept of division with two- and three-digit numbers.

Activity

Division. Display the transparency of page 20 on the projector and give students base ten blocks and page 20. Write $4\overline{)52}$ at the top of the page. Place five tens and two ones on the projector. Ask them to separate 52 into four groups using the spaces at the bottom of the page. Ask:

Can I give each group a ten? [yes] **So, 1 ten goes into each group. What do I have left?** [1 ten, 2 ones] **Can I give each group another ten?** [No, there is only 1 ten.] **Could I give each group some ones?** [No, there are only 2 ones.] **How can I divide 1 ten and 2 ones into four groups?** [regroup to 12 ones] **How many ones can I give each group?** [3 ones] **Do I have any blocks left?** [no] **How many blocks are there in each group?** [13] **What is $4\overline{)52}$?** [13]

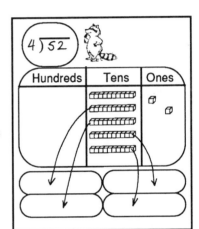

Try other problems such as $2\overline{)46}$ or $3\overline{)54}$. Also try problems such as $3\overline{)35}$ to obtain a quotient with a remainder. Assign some division problems with divisors 2, 3, and 4 so that students can use the format of page 20 to divide a given number accordingly. You may wish to challenge students with problems such as $4\overline{)132}$ or $3\overline{)222}$. Remove the transparency of page 20 to demonstrate division with divisors 5 through 9.

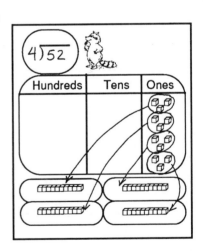

Practice

Assign various problems to be done on page 20. Observe students as they work with a partner and help each other divide the blocks into groups.

Wrap-Up

Call on volunteers to show their problems and to explain their solution methods. Emphasize the language associated with division problems as students give their explanations.

Try these problems:

$$3\overline{)87}^{[29]} \quad 4\overline{)85}^{[21r1]}$$

$$7\overline{)30}^{[4r2]} \quad 6\overline{)114}^{[19]}$$

Extension Activity

Let students try the division problems using play money. You may wish to give students page 48 for this activity.

Division

HUNDREDS	TENS	ONES

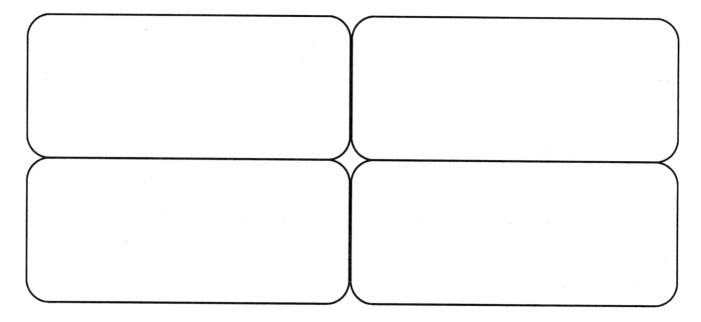

Overhead Manipulatives in Action, 3–6
© 1992 Learning Resources, Inc.

Hundred Board

Introduction

Using the *Hundred Board*, students can easily grasp important mathematical concepts involving counting, sequencing, and number patterns. Students can also learn some mental math techniques to help them quickly find sums and differences involving one- and two-digit numbers. The hundred board can also help students find common multiples of numbers and explore fractions with denominators of 100, decimals, and percentages.

Hundred Board Activities

Pages 25–26 Counting and Order
 27–28 High and Low
 29–30 Quick Sums and Differences
 31–32 Prime Numbers
 33–34 Fractions, Decimals, Percent

 Getting Organized

Materials you will need:
- ◆ *Overhead Hundred Board* (LER 475)
- ◆ *Transparent Counters* (LER 131)
- ◆ One transparency each of pages 22, 23, 24, 26, 28, 30, 32, 34
- ◆ Blank transparencies, overhead pens, paper

Materials students will need:
- ◆ *Hundred Boards* (LER 375), blank 10 × 10 grid on reverse side
- ◆ *Transparent Counters* (LER 131) or other colored counters
- ◆ Copies of pages 22, 23, 24, 26, 28, 30, 32, 34
- ◆ pencils, crayons or color markers, paper

Note: Make two copies of page 22 for each student—one copy to be used as a hundred board, the other copy to be cut into numbers 1–100 for use with the 10 × 10 grid on page 23. Also, page 24 may be used horizontally as shown or turned a quarter turn to be used showing vertical strips.

 Getting Started

Distribute a hundred board or page 22 to students. Call on students one at a time to read a particular row or column. Be sure that they can find numbers quickly on the hundred board. For example,

Say the numbers in the first row.
Say the numbers in the second column.
Say the numbers in reverse order in the last row.
Say the even numbers in the sixth row.
Say the odd numbers in reverse order in the third row.
Say the numbers that form the diagonal from 1 to 100.
Say the numbers that form the diagonal from 10 to 91.
Say the numbers with a 9 in the tens place.
Say the numbers with a 7 in the ones place.

With an exercise like the one above, students can review counting, counting on, counting back, skip counting, ordinal numbers, and place value concepts. You may wish to designate a student to act as a timer, complete with stop watch, to time each participant for each task. For example, each row or column must be said in less than 8 or 10 seconds.

The Hundred Board

1	2	3	4	5	6	7	8	9	10
11	12	13	14	15	16	17	18	19	20
21	22	23	24	25	26	27	28	29	30
31	32	33	34	35	36	37	38	39	40
41	42	43	44	45	46	47	48	49	50
51	52	53	54	55	56	57	58	59	60
61	62	63	64	65	66	67	68	69	70
71	72	73	74	75	76	77	78	79	80
81	82	83	84	85	86	87	88	89	90
91	92	93	94	95	96	97	98	99	100

One Hundred Squares

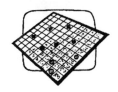

Overhead Manipulatives in Action, 3–6
© 1992 Learning Resources, Inc.

Hundred Board

Missing Numbers

Overhead Manipulatives in Action, 3–6
© 1992 Learning Resources, Inc.

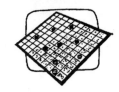

Counting and Order

 **Objectives**

To count on and to count back.
To find numbers before and after a given number.

Vocabulary

count, before, after, less than, greater than

Materials

Overhead Hundred Board, transparencies of pages 24 and 26, blank transparencies, overhead pens, paper; *Hundred Boards*, student copies of pages 24 and 26, number squares 1–100, pencils, scissors

Warm-Up

Missing Numbers. Distribute the hundred boards and copies of page 24 to students. Fill in some numbers in each of the six rows on the transparency of page 24 and display it on the projector with a sheet of paper covering all but the top row on the page. As you uncover each row, ask students to use the number clues to complete each row. Ask questions about a particular row such as, **Which numbers come before 42?** or **Which numbers come after 45?** Then repeat the exercise with other sets of number sequences, but this time turn the transparency for page 24 a quarter turn and present columns of numbers.

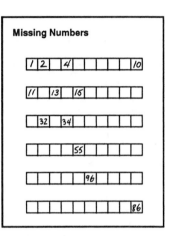

Activity 1

What's Missing? Distribute page 26 and display a transparency of the page on the projector. This activity is somewhat more difficult in that only part of a row or column is displayed which requires students to count on, count back, and to determine the order of the numbers. Fill in each partial row or column with one or two numbers and then ask students to fill in the rest of the numbers.

Activity 2

Hidden Numbers. Cut out the strips on page 26 to use as "cover up" strips in this activity. Display the *Overhead Hundred Board* on the projector. Place one or more cover strips on the hundred board and ask students to tell which numbers are hidden. Ask, **Which number comes just after 26?** if 27 and 28 are covered.

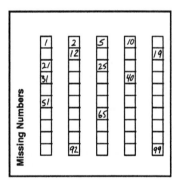

Practice

Pairs or small groups of students can challenge each other playing *What's Missing* by making up number sequences to be completed. Have them use number squares 1–100 to make the page reusable for each turn. Students can also play *Hidden Numbers* with each other.

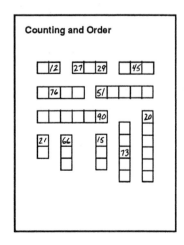

Wrap-Up

Ask students how the counting differed in the rows (counting by ones) than in the columns (counting by tens).

Extension Activity

Ask students to create a Number Scrabble game using the hundred board and number squares 1–100.

Counting and Order

Overhead Manipulatives in Action, 3–6
© 1992 Learning Resources, Inc.

High and Low

Objective

To find minimum and maximum numbers in number puzzle arrays.

Vocabulary

minimum, maximum

Materials

Overhead Hundred Board, transparency of page 28, blank transparencies, overhead pens; *Hundred Boards*, student copies of page 28, number squares 1–100, pencils, scissors

Warm-Up

Fill in only one or two numbers in the number puzzle arrays on the transparency of page 28 and display it on the projector. Distribute copies of page 28 to students and ask them to complete the puzzles. They may use their hundred boards as a reference. Discuss the solutions.

Activity

High and Low. Using the number puzzle arrays on page 28, challenge students to find as many ways as possible to complete each array. Assign a number array to each small group of students. Ask each group to find all the possible solutions for their array. Have students give the minimum and the maximum numbers for each array. For example, some of the solutions for the "T" array are:

Minimum numbers	Maximum numbers	Another solution
1 2 3	68 69 70	36 37 38
12	79	47
22	89	57
32	99	67

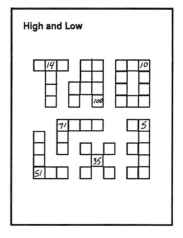

High and Low

Practice

Ask students to find and record all the solutions for each number puzzle. Ask them to predict what the minimum number could be for the letter "L" array or the number "3" array. Ask whether the number 100 could be used as the maximum number in any of the number puzzle arrays.

Wrap-Up

Have each student present at least one solution to the rest of the class.

Extension Activity

Students can play *Hidden Numbers* (found on page 25), or, have them find the sums of the number puzzle arrays.

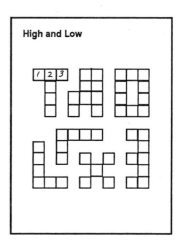

High and Low

High and Low

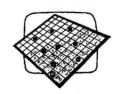

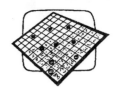

Quick Sums and Differences

 Objectives

To find sums quickly adding tens and ones.
To find differences quickly subtracting tens and ones.

Vocabulary

mental math

Materials

Overhead Hundred Board or transparency of page 30, *Transparent Counters*, blank transparencies, overhead pens; *Hundred Boards*, student copies of page 30, counters

Warm-Up

Place Value Review. Write several two-digit numbers on the projector. Ask students to tell how many tens and ones are in each number and to write them in expanded notation. For example, in 26 there are 2 tens and 6 ones and can be written as 20 + 6. Numbers that have 8 or 9 in the ones place can be written as:

$$28 = 20 + 8 \text{ or } 30 - 2$$
$$79 = 70 + 9 \text{ or } 80 - 1$$

Using the subtraction expression to represent a number with 8 or 9 in the ones place will help students find sums and differences quickly on the hundred board.

Activity

Quick Sums and Differences. Display the overhead hundred board or the transparency of page 30 on the projector. Distribute hundred boards or page 30 and counters. Ask students to move a counter on the hundred board to do the following:

◆ Counter on 24, add 5. [29; moved 5 spaces right]
◆ Counter on 47, subtract 3. [44; moved 3 spaces left]
◆ Counter on 16, add 30. [46; moved down 3 spaces]
◆ Counter on 73, subtract 40. [33; moved 4 spaces up]
◆ Counter on 26, add 43. [69; since 43 is 40 + 3, moved down 4 spaces and right 3 spaces]

Ask students to describe the moves they made to find each answer. Continue with other problems. For a problem like 35 + 29, show students how to move down three spaces and left one space since 29 can be considered as 30 – 1.

Practice

Continue with other addition and subtraction problems to enable students to gain speed in using the hundred chart to find sums and differences less than 100.

Wrap-Up

Have the students discuss or write about their "mental math" techniques developed on the hundred board to help them find sums and differences quickly. Key in on fast ways to add and subtract with 9 and 11.

Extension Activity

Have students find sums and differences involving three-digit numbers. Try problems like 357 + 203 and 589 – 299.

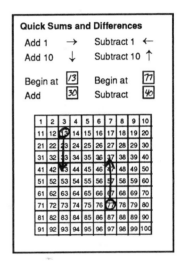

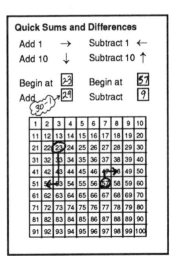

Quick Sums and Differences

Add 1	→		Subtract 1	←
Add 10	↓		Subtract 10	↑
Begin at	☐		Begin at	☐
Add	☐		Subtract	☐

1	2	3	4	5	6	7	8	9	10
11	12	13	14	15	16	17	18	19	20
21	22	23	24	25	26	27	28	29	30
31	32	33	34	35	36	37	38	39	40
41	42	43	44	45	46	47	48	49	50
51	52	53	54	55	56	57	58	59	60
61	62	63	64	65	66	67	68	69	70
71	72	73	74	75	76	77	78	79	80
81	82	83	84	85	86	87	88	89	90
91	92	93	94	95	96	97	98	99	100

Overhead Manipulatives in Action, 3–6
© 1992 Learning Resources, Inc.

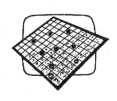

Prime Numbers

Objective
To identify prime numbers less than 100.

Vocabulary
prime number, factors, even number, composite number

Materials
Overhead Hundred Board, Transparent Counters, several colored overhead pens; *Hundred Boards*, student copies of page 32, counters, crayons or markers, pencils

Warm-Up
Give small groups of students hundred boards and counters. Display the *Overhead Hundred Board* on the projector. Ask students to use counters of one color to cover all even numbers or all numbers that have 2 as a factor. Ask, **What are factors of every even number?** [1, 2] **If you found all the numbers that have 2 as a factor, did you also find all the numbers that have 4 as a factor?** [Yes, numbers that have 4 as a factor also have 2 as a factor.] **Did you find all the numbers that have 8 as a factor?** [yes] **Did you find all the numbers that have 3 as a factor?** [no]

Activity
Prime Numbers. Give students page 32 and tell them that they will use it to record all the prime numbers they find. Ask students to cover all the numbers that have 2 as a factor with counters then lightly color these boxes with a crayon. Tell them that 2 is the first prime number. Define prime number for students: *A prime number is any number greater than 1 that has itself and 1 as its only factors. All other numbers are composite numbers.* Have students write a 2 in the first blank at the bottom of the page. Then ask students to cover all the numbers that have 3 as a factor and color these boxes with another color crayon. Ask, **What are the factors of 3?** [1, 3] **Is 3 a prime number? Why or why not?** [Yes, its only factors are 1 and 3.] Have students write 3 on the bottom of the page. **Is 4 a prime number? Why or why not?** [No, it is shaded so it has a number other than 1 and 4 as a factor.] Help students find all the multiples of 5, then write 5 as a prime number on page 32.

Practice
Students can continue covering all the numbers that have seven, eleven, thirteen, and so on as a factor, until they find all the prime numbers less than 100.

Wrap-Up
After students have found all of the prime numbers less than 100, tell them that they have just completed the Sieve of Erathosthenes. Erathosthenes was an astronomer in 200 B.C. who discovered this method for finding prime numbers.

Extension Activity
Ask students to predict how many prime numbers there are between 100 and 200, 200 and 300, and so on. If a computer is available, help students write a program to make a list of prime numbers.

The prime numbers less than 100:
2, 3, 5, 7, 11, 13, 17, 19, 23, 29, 31, 37, 41, 43, 47, 53, 59, 61, 67, 71, 73, 79, 83, 89, 97

Prime Numbers

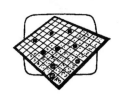

1	2	3	4	5	6	7	8	9	10
11	12	13	14	15	16	17	18	19	20
21	22	23	24	25	26	27	28	29	30
31	32	33	34	35	36	37	38	39	40
41	42	43	44	45	46	47	48	49	50
51	52	53	54	55	56	57	58	59	60
61	62	63	64	65	66	67	68	69	70
71	72	73	74	75	76	77	78	79	80
81	82	83	84	85	86	87	88	89	90
91	92	93	94	95	96	97	98	99	100

A prime number is any number greater than 1 that has itself and 1 as its only factors.

Overhead Manipulatives in Action, 3–6
© 1992 Learning Resources, Inc.

Fractions, Decimals, Percent

 Objectives

To understand fractions, decimals, and percents using the hundred board.
To relate fractions, decimals, and percents to each other using the hundred board.

Vocabulary

fraction, decimal, percent, per hundred, hundredths

Materials

Overhead Hundred Board, Transparent Counters, transparency of page 34, blank transparencies, overhead pens; *Hundred Boards*, student copies of page 34, counters, pencils

Warm-Up

Distribute hundred boards and counters. Display the *Overhead Hundred Board* on the projector. Ask students to cover numbers 1–50 with counters. Then ask the following types of questions:

> **What fraction of the board is covered?** [1/2 or 50/100]
> **What percent of the board is covered?** [50%]
> **How many hundredths are covered?** [50/100 or 0.50]

Now place the transparency of page 34 on the projector. Shade the boxes for numbers 1–50 on the hundred board. Ask students to help you write the fraction, decimal, and percent for the amount that is shaded. [50/100, 0.50, 50%] Ask students to give the simplest fraction. [1/2] Then ask them to think of another way to shade 50% (or 1/2) of the hundred board. Solutions may include all the even numbers or all the odd numbers.

Activity

Fractions, Decimals, Percents. These exercises will reinforce the concept of fractions, decimals, and percents, and review whole number concepts.

Find the fraction, decimal, and percent for each of these problems.

1. **All the numbers in any three columns of the hundred chart.** [30/100 or 3/10, 0.30 or 0.3, 30%]
2. **All the numbers with a 6 in the tens place.** [10/100 or 1/10, 0.10 or 0.1, 10%]
3. **All the prime numbers.** [25/100 or 1/4, 0.25, 25%]

Practice

Make up more problems for students to do. Encourage them to create, share, and then solve problems on their own. Give students several copies of page 34.

Wrap-Up

Discuss the solutions for each problem. Ask students whether they can express the fraction in simpler terms instead of the fraction □/100. Have a class discussion to talk about the relationship between fractions, decimals, and percents.

Extension Activity

Ask students to color designs on copies of the hundred board (page 22) or copies of the one hundred squares grid (page 23) and challenge other students to find the fractional part of the board that is covered by the design.

Fractions, Decimals, Percents

1	2	3	4	5	6	7	8	9	10
11	12	13	14	15	16	17	18	19	20
21	22	23	24	25	26	27	28	29	30
31	32	33	34	35	36	37	38	39	40
41	42	43	44	45	46	47	48	49	50
51	52	53	54	55	56	57	58	59	60
61	62	63	64	65	66	67	68	69	70
71	72	73	74	75	76	77	78	97	80
81	82	83	84	85	86	87	88	89	90
91	92	93	94	95	96	97	98	99	10

$$\frac{\boxed{}}{100}$$

Overhead Manipulatives in Action, 3–6
© 1992 Learning Resources, Inc.

Bills and Coins

Introduction

Using play money bills and coins gives students the opportunity to learn about money, and reinforces important number concepts and operation skills. The play money will enable students to learn the value of each bill and coin, find dollar and coin equivalences, count amounts of money, combine amounts of money and make change. Incorporating money-oriented activities into the mathematics curriculum lends itself especially well to develop mental math skills as students will not necessarily have calculators and pencil and paper to find sums of money or to make change in real situations.

Bills and Coins Activities

Getting Organized

Materials you will need:
- ◆ *Overhead Coins* (LER 625)
- ◆ *Overhead Bills* (LER 635)
- ◆ One transparency each of pages 42, 44, 46, 48, 50
- ◆ Blank transparencies, overhead pens, paper

Materials students will need:
- ◆ *Coin Set* (LER 101; *Coins in bulk* LER 95–99)
- ◆ *Paper Money in Wallet Set* (LER 104; *Paper money in bulk* LER 91–94)
- ◆ Copies of pages 36, 37, 38, 39, 40, 42, 44, 46, 48, 50
- ◆ Crayons or color markers, scissors, paper

Duplicate pages 38, 39 and 40 on light green paper if possible to make the dollar-bill cutouts seem more realistic. Make several copies of these pages for each student.

Getting Started

Distribute small amounts of play money to each student or have them color and cut out bills and coins (pages 36–40). Review the names and values of the coins: penny, 1¢; nickel, 5¢; dime, 10¢; quarter, 25¢; half dollar, 50¢. Have students put the coins in order from greatest to least value. Show two, three, or four coins on the projector and ask students to find the total value of the group of coins. Introduce the bills one at a time. Discuss the value of the $1, $5, $10, and $20 bills. Have students find coin equivalents for the $1 bill. Then have them find dollar-bill equivalents for larger bills. Discuss the features found on the front and back of each bill:

$1 bill	George Washington/The Great Seal	$20 bill	Andrew Jackson/The White House
$5 bill	Abraham Lincoln/Lincoln Memorial	$50 bill	Ulysses S. Grant/U.S. Capitol
$10 bill	Alexander Hamilton/U.S. Treasury	$100 bill	Benjamin Franklin/Independence Hall

Have students find out how the system of using money developed, when the first coins and paper money were used, how the U.S. Treasury works, and what is involved in minting coins and printing bills.

Pennies and Nickels

Overhead Manipulatives in Action, 3–6
© 1992 Learning Resources, Inc.

Dimes, Quarters, and Half-Dollars

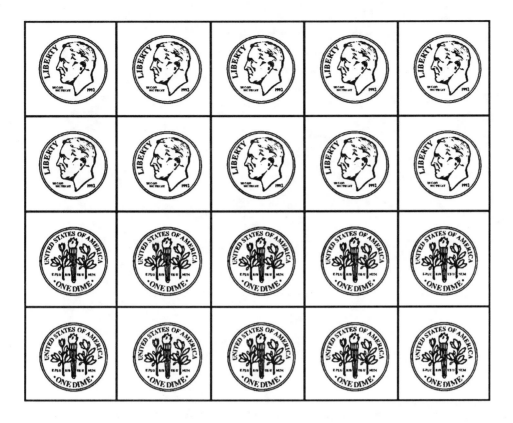

$1, $5 Dollar Bills

Overhead Manipulatives in Action, 3–6
© 1992 Learning Resources, Inc.

$10, $20 Dollar Bills

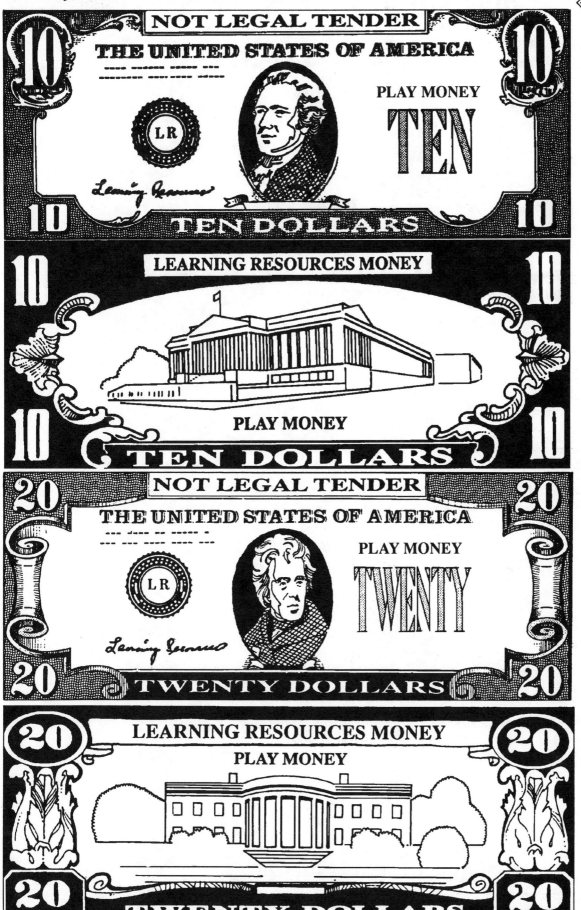

$50, $100 Dollar Bills

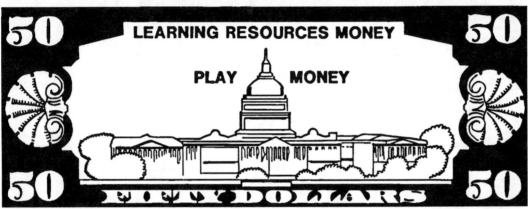

Overhead Manipulatives in Action, 3–6
© 1992 Learning Resources, Inc.

Counting Money

 **Objective**

To count amounts of money.

Vocabulary

count, amount

Materials

Overhead Bills and Coins, transparency of page 42, blank transparencies, overhead pens; play money, student copies of page 42, pencils, paper bags

Warm-Up

Lead students in some *skip counting* and *counting on* exercises. Have them count by fives and tens. Then ask them to count on by ones, fives, and tens from a given number.

Activity 1

Counting with Dollar Bills. Distribute play money to students and copies of page 42. Display the transparency of page 42 on the projector and some $1, $5, and $10 bills. As students follow along, count the bills on the projector beginning with the bills of greatest value—$10 bills, then $5 bills, then $1 bills.

Activity 2

Counting Bills and Coins. Show some $1 bills and two or three coins on the projector and ask volunteers how they would count this money. Students should understand that the counting process should start with the bills and then proceed with the coins in descending order. For example, for three $1 bills, two dimes and a quarter, count and say $1, $2, $3, $3.25, $3.35, $3.45. Present several other amounts of money on the projector to include $5, $10, and $20 bills as well as the $1 bills and coins.

Practice

Pairs of students can use play money and copies of page 42 to count amounts of money. Ask students to put the bills in one paper bag and the coins in another paper bag. In turn, students can draw a handful of bills and coins from each bag and count the total amount of money.

Wrap-Up

Ask for volunteers to help you count amounts of money at the projector. Pay attention to their organization and counting techniques.

Extension Activity

Challenge students to find as many ways as they can to find coin equivalents for a $1 bill.

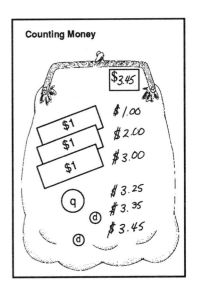

Counting Money

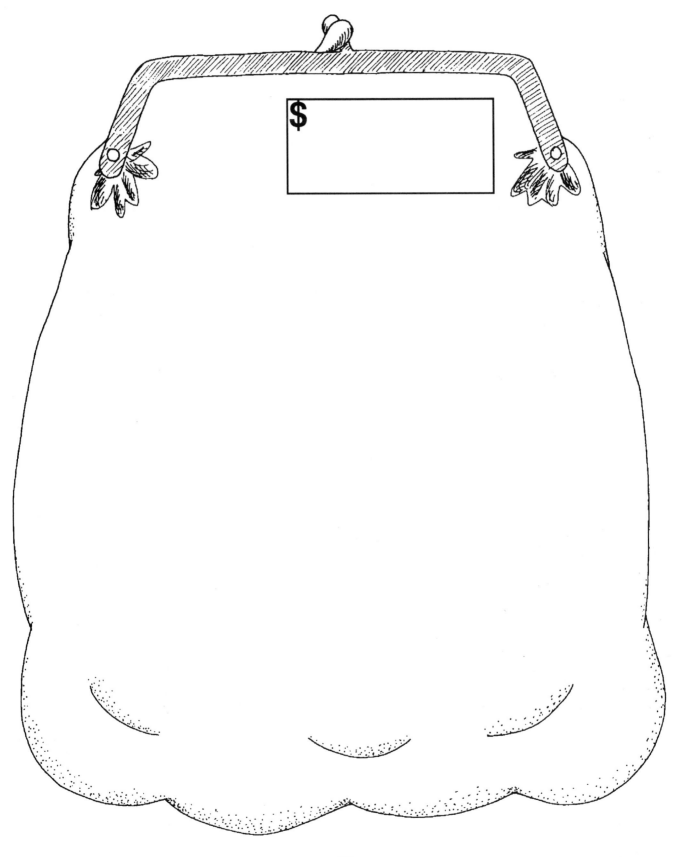

$

Overhead Manipulatives in Action, 3–6
© 1992 Learning Resources, Inc.

Going Shopping

 Objectives

To match amounts of money to written amounts.
To find the total amount of money for two or more purchased items. (addition)

Vocabulary

total, amount

Materials

Overhead Bills and Coins, transparency of page 44, blank transparencies, overhead pens; play money, student copies of page 44, pencils

Warm-Up

Initiate a discussion about shopping. Bring some catalogs, sale pages from newspapers, and menus to class. Since most or all of the students have probably accompanied a family member or friend, or have even made purchases themselves, ask them how things are purchased and paid for.

Activity 1

Matching Amounts of Money to Written Amounts. Distribute play money and page 44. Display the transparency of page 44 on the projector. Circle one of the items. Ask students how much it costs and which bills and coins are needed to pay for it. Stress that it is most efficient to use the least number of bills and coins. After the bills and coins are shown on the bottom of the page and counted aloud, write the amount in the box.

Activity 2

Finding the Total Amount. Ask a volunteer to choose two items to buy on page 44 and circle the items on the transparency. Write the two amounts above the answer box at the bottom of the page. Have another volunteer show the bills and coins for each item, then combine the play money to find the sum. Students can trade to show the amount with the least amount of bills and coins. Continue with other examples.

Practice

Students can work in pairs to play Store, playing the roles of buyer and store keeper. Have them find the total amount of money for two, three, and even all four items shown on page 44. The buyer should perform the addition and figure out the amount of bills and coins to be paid; the store keeper should check the addition and recount the money.

Wrap-Up

Discuss the activity. Have students write addition problems about the items on page 44 in the space provided at the bottom of the page. Exchange the problems with other students.

Extension Activity

Provide newspaper advertisements and catalogs for students to find how much it will cost to buy a complete outfit or a computer system. Some students may even wish to include tax and shipping charges.

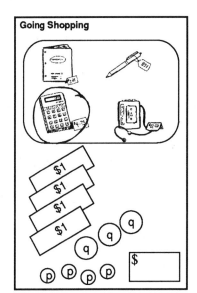

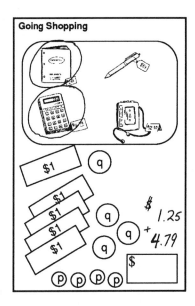

Going Shopping

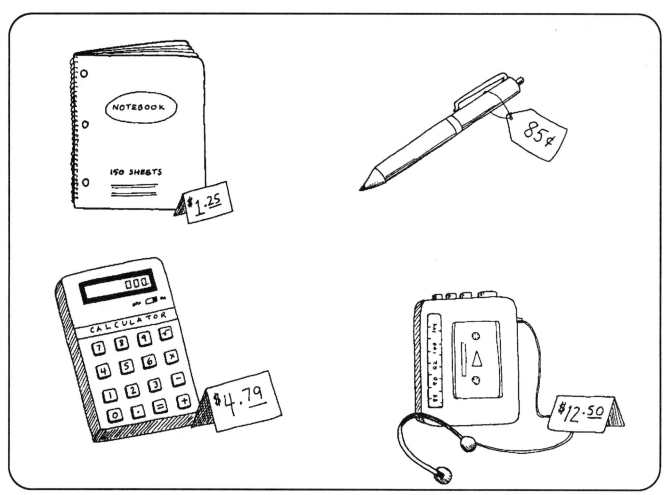

Overhead Manipulatives in Action, 3–6
© 1992 Learning Resources, Inc.

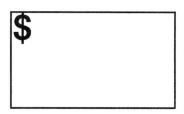

Making Change

Objectives

To give the exact amount of bills and coins needed to make a purchase.
To figure out the closest amount of bills or bills and coins to make a purchase.
To make change.

Vocabulary

making change

Materials

Overhead Bills and Coins, transparency of page 46, blank transparencies,
overhead pens; play money, student copies of page 46, pencils

Warm-Up

Having Enough Money. Distribute play money and page 46. Display the
transparency of page 46 on the projector and place a blank transparency over it.
Circle or check two items on the menu and ask if these can be purchased for
$2.00 or $4.00, and so on. (Disregard sales tax at this time.) Examples:
Can a slice of pizza and a carton of milk be purchased for $2.00? [yes]
Can yogurt and french fries be purchased for $2.00? [no]

Activity 1

Change from Bills. Choose an item to purchase from the menu on page 46 and
ask students to pay for it with a $1, $5, $10, or $20 bill. For example, ask, **How
much change will you get if you pay for an order of french fries with a $1
bill?** [$.20] **If you pay for a cheeseburger with a $10 bill?** [$8.05] Make the
activity more challenging by purchasing several items, finding the total amount,
and then getting the correct change.

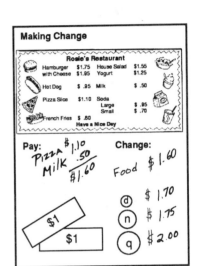

Activity 2

Change from Bills and Coins. Follow the same procedure as for Activity 1, the
only difference being that volunteers can pay with bills and coins.

Practice

Let pairs of students work as a customer in a restaurant and a restaurant owner.
The customer orders one or more items, and the owner totals up the items. The
customer gives the owner the exact or an adequate amount of money, and the
owner finds and counts out the change. The restaurant owner may use a
calculator to act as a cash register to total the bill.

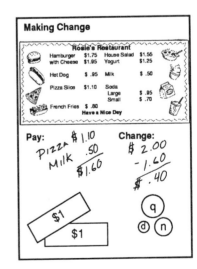

Wrap-Up

Discuss the activity with students. Have each student write and solve a problem
at the bottom of page 46 using the information in the menu.

Extension Activity

Obtain a sales tax chart for students and have them figure out their purchases
with sales tax.

Making Change

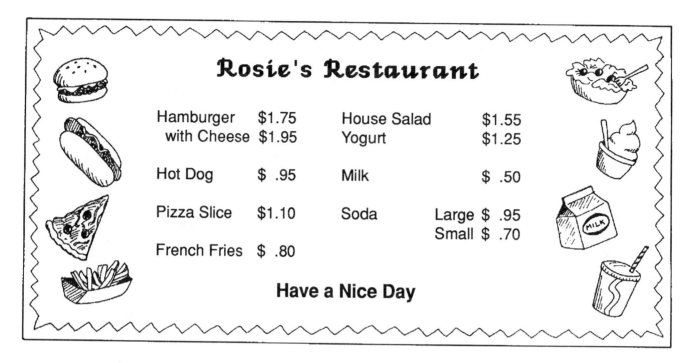

Rosie's Restaurant

Hamburger	$1.75	House Salad		$1.55
with Cheese	$1.95	Yogurt		$1.25
Hot Dog	$ .95	Milk		$ .50
Pizza Slice	$1.10	Soda	Large	$ .95
			Small	$ .70
French Fries	$ .80			

Have a Nice Day

Pay: **Change:**

Bunches of Money

 Objective

To find the total amount of multiple sets of money. (multiplication)

Vocabulary

multiply

Materials

Overhead Bills and Coins, transparencies of pages 46 and 48, blank transparencies, overhead pens; play money, student copies of pages 46 and 48, pencils, calculators

Warm-Up

Display the transparency of page 46 with the following problems:

1. **Buy 3 hot dogs** [about $3.00; $2.85]
2. **Buy 2 cheeseburgers** [about $4.00; $3.90]
3. **Buy 5 large sodas** [about $5.00; $4.75]
4. **Buy 3 salads** [about $5.00; $4.65]

Ask students to estimate, then find the total amount for each problem. Students may use calculators.

Activity

Bunches of Money. Distribute play money and pages 46 and 48. Display the transparency of page 48 on the projector. Write $.95 × 3 in the problem box. This represents problem 1 in the *Warm-Up* (buy 3 hot dogs). Ask students what the problem means and how they can show the problem using money. [Place 3 sets of $.95 on page 48.] Ask students to use their play money to find the total amount of the 3 sets of $.95 and then make dollar and coin equivalent "trades" to express the amount with the least amount of bills and coins. To have the least bills and coins, students should show: 2 $1 bills, 3 quarters, and 1 dime totaling $2.85. Do problem 2, then assign problems 3 and 4 as practice.

Practice

Have students complete problems 3 and 4. More problems may be assigned. You may also use the items illustrated on page 44.

Wrap-Up

Discuss the problems. Ask volunteers to show and describe how they found the solutions.

Extension Activity

Challenge students to find the cost of one item for all the members of their family or all the members of the class. For example, how much would 24 hamburgers cost?

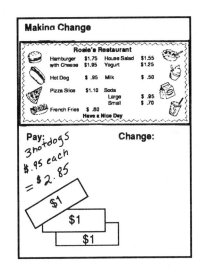

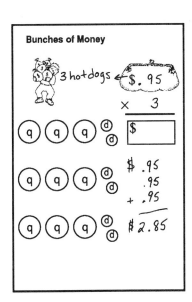

Bunches of Money

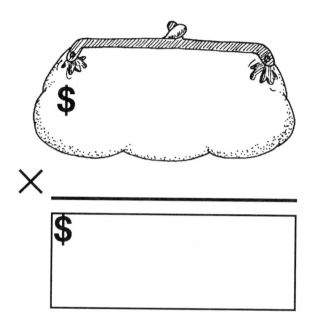

Overhead Manipulatives in Action, 3–6
© 1992 Learning Resources, Inc.

Divvy It Up!

✓ Objective
To divide amounts of money into equivalent sets. (division)

Vocabulary
divide, share

Materials
Overhead Bills and Coins, transparency of page 50, blank transparencies, overhead pens; play money, student copies of page 50, pencils

Warm-Up
Distribute play money to groups of four students. Show $.56 (2 quarters, 1 nickel, 1 penny) on the projector. Ask students to pair up within their group and share $.56. **How much will each pair get?** [$.28] **What did you have to do to share the $.56 equally?** [Trade the nickel for 5 pennies, then each pair will get 1 quarter and 3 pennies.] Next, ask students to share $.56 between the four members of their group. **What did you have to do to share the $.56 equally?** [Trade 2 quarters for five dimes (each gets a dime). With 1 dime, 1 nickel, and 1 penny left, trade them for 16 pennies and give each student 4 pennies for a total of $.14 per student.] Ask the students what happens when three students try to share $.56. [$.18 each with $.02 left over]

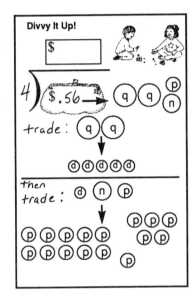

Activity
Divvy It Up! Distribute page 50 and display the transparency of page 50 on the projector. Write $5.40 in the "purse" and 2 as the divisor. (First try a divisor of 2, and then 3 and 4.) With students working in groups of four, have them find their "fair shares." [For two students, $2.70; for three students, $1.80; for four students, $1.35]

Practice
Assign other dollar-and-cent amounts to be divided among two, three, or four students. Ask students to write about the procedure for dividing up the money on the back of their paper.

Wrap-Up
Ask students to demonstrate the division process using amounts of money. Try divisors of 5, 6, 7, 8, and 9.

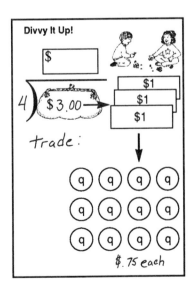

Extension Activity
Bring in a pizza menu from a local restaurant. Tell students to pretend they are buying a pizza and soft drinks for three people. Ask them to find their share of the bill. Students can also use a sales tax chart or find the sales tax to be included in the bill. Some students might also include a tip.

Divvy It Up!

$

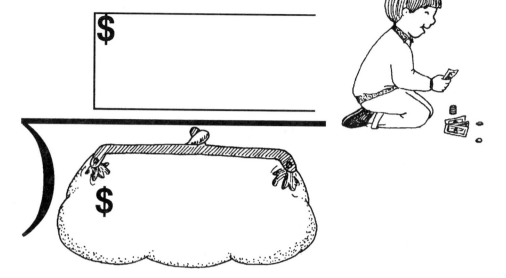

$

Overhead Manipulatives in Action, 3–6
© 1992 Learning Resources, Inc.

Pattern Blocks

Introduction

Pattern Blocks are especially effective when learning about geometric shapes and relationships, creating patterns, finding lines of symmetry, and exploring fraction concepts. By using the pattern blocks to create various shapes and mosaic designs, students will also have the opportunity to gain an aesthetic as well as a quantitative appreciation for the blocks. The pattern block set consists of six shapes in six colors—*orange square, green triangle, red trapezoid, yellow hexagon, blue parallelogram* and *tan (or clear) rhombus.* (*NOTE*: For clarity, we will call the blue shape a parallelogram although it is also a rhombus.)

Pattern Block Activities

Pages 55–56 Ways to Make Yellow
57–58 Finding Fractions
59–60 Exploring Symmetry
61–62 Slides, Turns, Flips
63–64 Analyzing Angles

 Getting Organized

Materials you will need:

◆ *Overhead Pattern Blocks* (LER 640)
◆ One transparency each of pages 53, 54, 56, 58, 60, 62, 64
◆ Blank transparencies, overhead pens, paper

Materials students will need:

◆ *Pattern Blocks* (Plastic LER 134, Wood LER 334)
◆ *Pattern Block Stickers* (LER 268)
◆ Copies of pages 52, 53, 54, 56, 58, 60, 62, 64
◆ Crayons or color markers, scissors, paste, pencils, paper

 Getting Started

Give pairs or small groups of students a set of pattern blocks. If pattern blocks are not available, have students color and cut out the shapes shown on page 52. Ask them to sort the pattern blocks by color. Then ask them about the color and shape of the pattern blocks. Display pattern blocks on the projector and ask:

What color is the square? [orange]
What color is the triangle? [green]
Which shape is yellow? [hexagon]
Which blocks have three sides? [triangles]
Which blocks have four sides? [square, parallelogram, rhombus, trapezoid]
Are there any blocks with five sides? [no] **Six sides?** [yes, hexagon]
Look at the blocks with four sides. These are *quadrilaterals.*
Do some of these shapes have special features? [a square has equal and parallel sides and right angles; a parallelogram has two pairs of parallel sides; a rhombus has equal and parallel sides; a trapezoid has one pair of parallel sides]
Do you think a square is a special type of rhombus? [yes, a rhombus with right angles]

After talking about the attributes of each pattern block, let students use the blocks to make various shapes and designs. Challenge them to make an animal, a letter of the alphabet, a person, a rocket, or a plant. After manipulating the blocks for a short time, students will discover that all of the sides of each block are the same length and that any two adjacent blocks can fit snugly together.

Pattern Blocks

yellow

red

green

orange

blue

tan

Pattern Block Grid

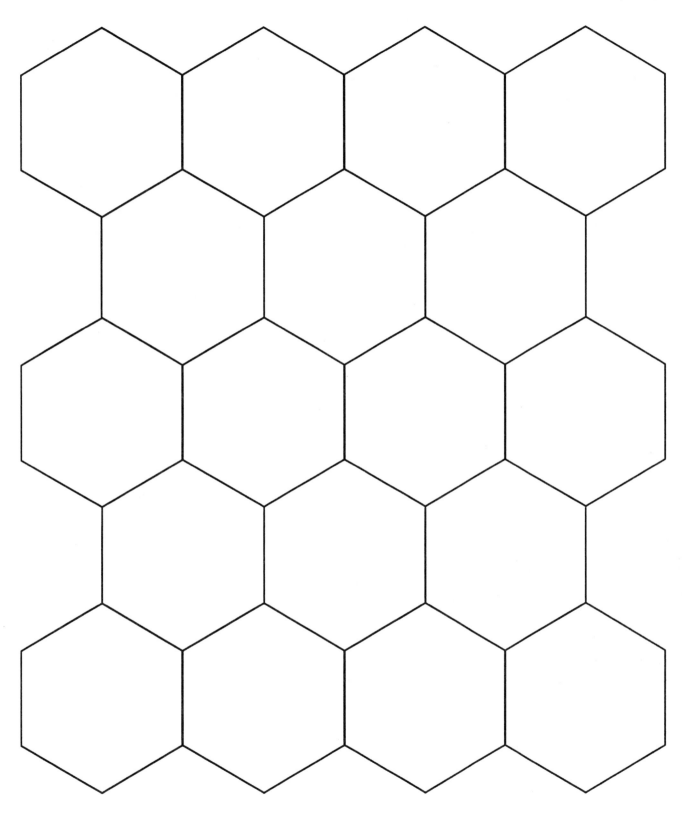

Isometric Grid

Overhead Manipulatives in Action, 3–6
© 1992 Learning Resources, Inc.

Ways to Make Yellow

 **Objective**

To create a pattern block shape using other pattern blocks.

Vocabulary

square, triangle, parallelogram, rhombus, trapezoid, hexagon

Materials

Overhead Pattern Blocks, transparency of page 56; *Pattern Blocks*, student copies of page 56, pencils, crayons

Warm-Up

Give pattern blocks to students. Display the blue parallelogram on the projector. Ask about its color and shape. Then ask students to find two blocks that will make the same shape. [2 green triangles] Next place the red trapezoid on the projector and ask about its color and shape. Ask students to find two other ways to make the trapezoid. [3 green triangles; 1 green triangle and 1 blue parallelogram]

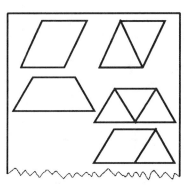

Activity

Ways to Make Yellow. Display the yellow hexagon on the projector and ask about its color and shape. Ask students to find another way to make the hexagon. Show only one solution on the projector. Next, distribute page 56 and place the transparency of page 56 on the projector. Challenge students to find nine ways to make a hexagon.

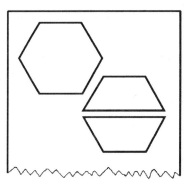

Practice

Have students work in pairs to complete page 56. Ask them to record their solutions on the page by drawing the lines and coloring the shapes of the pattern blocks used.

Wrap-Up

When all students have finished finding the nine ways to make a hexagon, have students take turns displaying a solution on the projector. *Note*: Tell students to save their solutions from page 56 for the lesson about fractions on pages 57 and 58.

Extension Activity

Challenge students to make larger sizes of the pattern blocks. For example, four squares can make a larger square, a trapezoid and a triangle can make a larger triangle, and a hexagon and six trapezoids can make a larger hexagon.

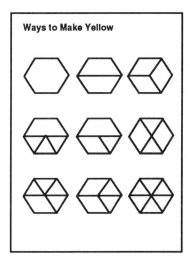

Ways to Make Yellow

Ways to Make Yellow

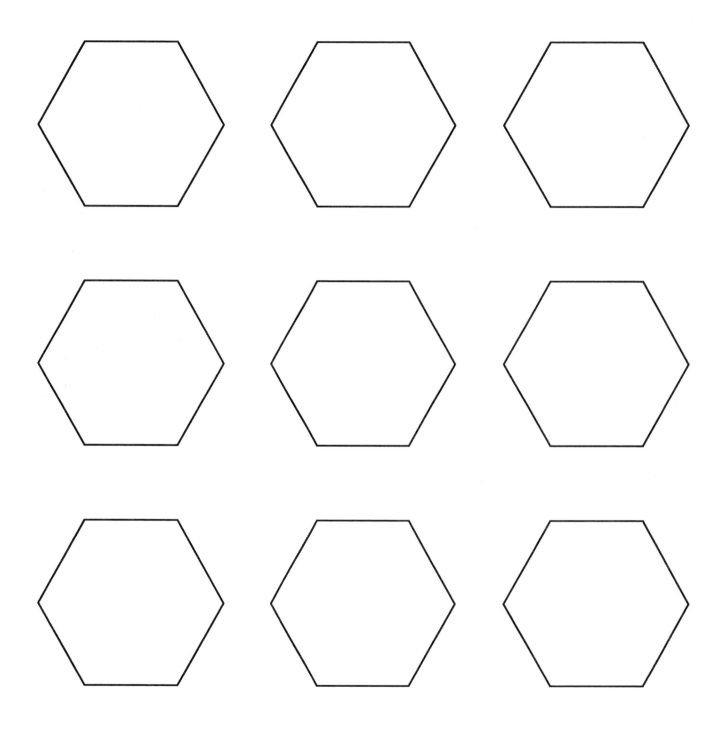

Overhead Manipulatives in Action, 3–6
© 1992 Learning Resources, Inc.

Finding Fractions

 Objective

To show and name fractional parts of a region.

Vocabulary

triangle, parallelogram, rhombus, trapezoid, hexagon

Materials

Overhead Pattern Blocks, transparency of page 58, blank transparencies, sheet of paper, overhead pens; *Pattern Blocks*, student copies of page 58, pencils

Warm-Up

Unit Fractions. Distribute pattern blocks and page 58. Display the transparency of page 58 on the projector. To focus on the hexagon at the top of the page, cover the rest of the page with a sheet of paper. As you point to the hexagon say: **This is one whole region. If I place a red trapezoid on the hexagon, what part of it is red?** [1/2] **How do you know?** [If 2 red blocks = 1, then 1 red block = 1/2.] Continue using the blue parallelogram [1/3 of the hexagon] and the green triangle [1/6 of the hexagon].

Proper Fractions. If students saved their solutions from page 56, tell them to label each hexagon with fractions describing the amount of color for it. (If students do not have page 56 completed, have them complete it at this time.) For example, if the hexagon was formed using 2 blue and 2 green blocks, then 2/3 is blue and 1/3 (or 2/6) is green.

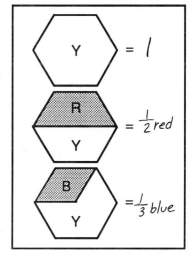

Activity

Finding Fractions. In this activity, the value of the hexagon will not necessarily represent one whole. Give students values for the trapezoid, parallelogram, or triangle and ask them to find the values of the other shapes. For example: **If the trapezoid represents 1, what is the value of the other shapes on the page?** [hexagon, 2; parallelogram, 2/3; triangle, 1/3]

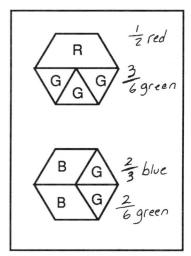

Practice

Continue the activity by asking students to find the whole number and fractional relationships for the following: **What is the value of each shape if the rhombus equals 1? Trapezoid equals 3? Triangle equals 1/3? Rhombus equals 1/2?** Let pairs of students work on a particular relationship.

Wrap-Up

Discuss the fractional number relationships. Ask students whether some of the solutions yielded mixed numbers as well as whole numbers and fractions.

Extension Activity

Ask students how they would show the mixed numbers 1 5/6 or 2 1/3 using the pattern blocks.

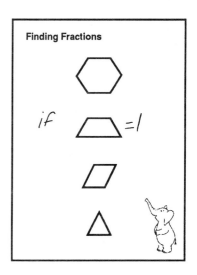

Finding Fractions

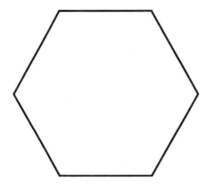

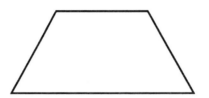

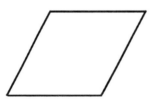

Pattern Blocks   58   Overhead Manipulatives in Action, 3–6
© 1992 Learning Resources, Inc.

Exploring Symmetry

  Objective

To find all lines of symmetry for each pattern block.

Vocabulary

fold line, symmetry, symmetric

Materials

Overhead Pattern Blocks, transparency of page 60, paper cutouts of pattern blocks; overhead pens; *Pattern Blocks*, student copies of pages 52 and 60, scissors, pencils

Warm-Up

Meaning of Symmetry. Talk about symmetric objects such as a valentine heart, the capital letter H, or the numeral 8. Ask students what each shape would look like when folded in half. Explain to them that the fold line is a line of symmetry for the shape and that the part on each side of the fold line is exactly the same size. When this happens, the shape is *symmetric*. Tell them that some shapes have more than one line of symmetry such as the capital letter H.

Making Guesses. Distribute pattern blocks and page 60. Ask students to guess how many lines of symmetry there are for each pattern block shape, then record their guess. Then distribute copies of page 52 and have students cut out one copy of each pattern block shape.

Activity

Finding Lines of Symmetry. Display the transparency of page 60 on the projector. Ask students to guess how many lines of symmetry are in the triangle. Record all guesses next to the triangle. Have students follow along as you take the triangle cutout and fold it in half (along its altitude, a perpendicular line from one angle to the opposite side) and record this line in one color on the triangle on page 60. Ask students if the triangle can be folded in half another way to find another line of symmetry. There are three lines of symmetry for this triangle. Record each line of symmetry in a different color.

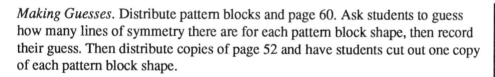

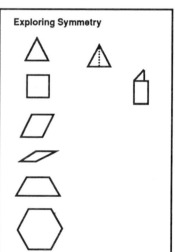

Practice

Ask students to find all the lines of symmetry for the remaining pattern block shapes shown on page 60 by folding each cutout. Have students record their results, then compare these with the guesses they recorded in the *Warm-Up* activity.

Wrap-Up

Discuss the solutions with the class. After all the lines of symmetry have been displayed by the students, ask them to think about the following: **Do all squares have four lines of symmetry?** [yes] **Do all triangles have three lines of symmetry?** [no, obtuse triangle has none, isosceles triangle has only one] **Do all trapezoids have a line of symmetry?** [no]

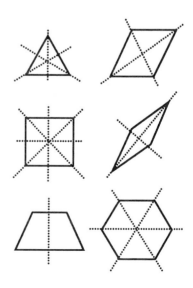

Exploring Symmetry

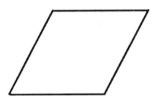

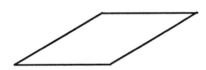

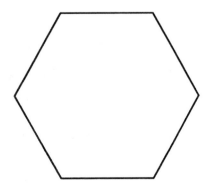

Overhead Manipulatives in Action, 3–6
© 1992 Learning Resources, Inc.

Slides, Turns, Flips

 Objectives

To show a translation (slide) of a pattern.
To show a rotation (turn) of a pattern.
To show a reflection (flip) of a pattern.
To form patterns using slides, turns, and/or flips.

Vocabulary

slide, turn, flip, tessellation

Materials

Overhead Pattern Blocks, transparencies of pages 53, 54, and 62; *Pattern Blocks, Pattern Block Stickers*, student copies of pages 53, 54, and 62, pencils and crayons or colored cutouts of the pattern blocks on page 52, paste

Warm-Up

Distribute pattern blocks and copies of page 53. Tell students to make a "quilt pattern" on page 53 using the pattern blocks. You may wish to show students how to begin by displaying the transparency of page 53 with an arrangement of pattern blocks. Have them record their patterns by using pattern block stickers or coloring and pasting pattern block cutouts from page 53. Display their creations on the bulletin board for all students to share. Discuss the patterns. Ask if some students repeated certain parts of the patterns in their quilt.

Activity

Slides, Turns, Flips. Give students copies of page 62 and display the transparency of page 62 on the projector. Show an example for each transformational pattern using the red, blue, and green blocks.

Slides. Show the red–blue–green pattern in the first hexagon. Ask students what the pattern will look like if it is moved (slid) to the next hexagonal outline. Have them find what the pattern would look like for the entire line. When a pattern is repeated in a line or on a grid (pages 53 or 54), a *tesselation* is formed.

Turns. Show the red–blue–green pattern in the first hexagon. Ask students what the pattern will look like if it is turned (rotated) 60° each time for three times. Ask if it will ever get back to the original pattern [yes, on the sixth turn]. Try a rotation of 180° to see what happens to the pattern. When does the original pattern appear again? [on the 2nd turn].

Flips. Show the red–blue–green pattern in the first hexagon. Ask students what the pattern will look like if it is reflected (flipped) to the next outline. Tell students to complete the row.

Practice

Direct students to create their own hexagonal patterns on page 62. Then give students three copies of page 53 to expand their patterns. Ask them to show one tesselation (slide), one rotational pattern (turn), and one reflected pattern (flip).

Wrap-Up

Discuss the patterns and display them in the classroom.

Overhead Manipulatives in Action, 3–6
© 1992 Learning Resources, Inc.

(61)

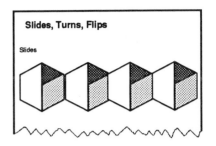

Slides, Turns, Flips

Slides

Turns

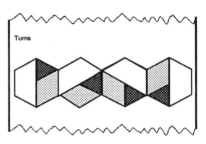

Slides, Turns, Flips

Slides

Turns

Flips

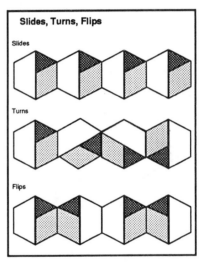

Pattern Block Grid

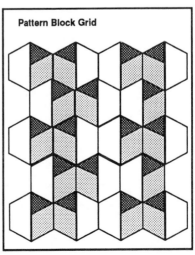

Pattern Blocks

Slides, Turns, Flips

Slides

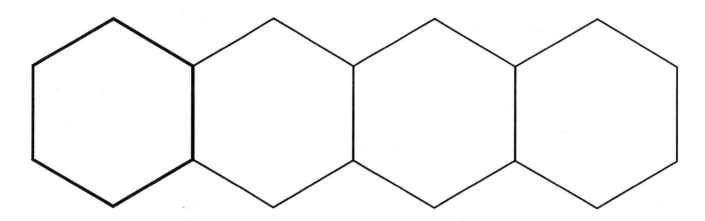

Turns

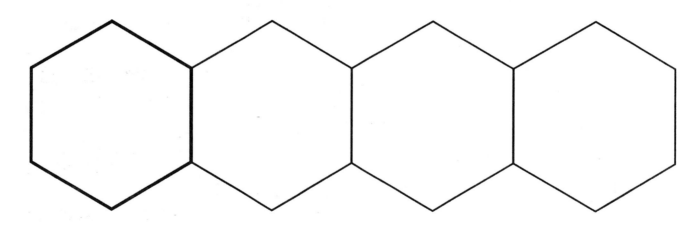

Flips

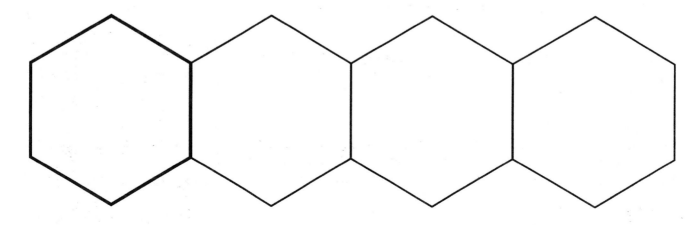

Overhead Manipulatives in Action, 3–6
© 1992 Learning Resources, Inc.

Analyzing Angles

✓ Objectives

To find the measure of each angle for each pattern block.
To find the sum of the angles for each pattern block.

Vocabulary

angle, degree, right, acute, obtuse, protractor

Materials

Overhead Pattern Blocks, transparency of page 64, blank transparencies,
overhead pen; *Pattern Blocks*, student copies of page 64, pencils

Warm-Up

Distribute the pattern blocks and page 64. Display the orange square on the
projector. Review the attributes of the square—equal sides, parallel sides, right
angles. Ask how many degrees are in a right angle [90°]. Place the blue
parallelogram next to the square. Review its attributes and ask about the size of
its angles. [some are more than 90°, some are less than 90°] Give students the
definitions of these angles: A *right angle* contains 90°, an *acute angle* is between
0° and 90° (such as 30° or 60°), and an *obtuse angle* is between 90° and 180°
(such as 120°or 150°). Students can record the definitions at the bottom of page
64, then give a more accurate description of the parallelogram, such as a shape
that contains a pair of acute and a pair of obtuse angles.

Activity

Analyzing Angles. Working with the pattern block shapes shown on page 64, ask
students to describe all of the angles of the blocks in terms of *right*, *acute*, and
obtuse angles. Then ask students to find the measure of each angle for each
block. Place a green triangle on the hexagonal outline. Ask: **How many degrees
are in a complete rotation (turn)?** [360°] **How many times must the green
triangle be rotated to form a complete rotation?** [6 times] **So, how many
degrees do you think are in each angle of this triangle?** [60°; 360° ÷ 6 = 60°]
To verify the angle measure, place the green triangle on the protractor at the
bottom of page 64. (Show students how to measure an angle with a protractor.)

Practice

Students can work in pairs or small groups to find the angle measure for each
pattern block and the sum of the angles for each pattern block. Then have them
record the results next to each shape on page 64.

Wrap-Up

Discuss the results of the practice activities with students.

Extension Activity

Have students find the angle measures of each tangram piece and various
figures formed on a geoboard.

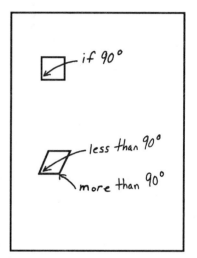

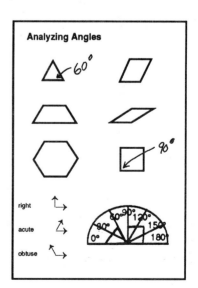

Shape	Angle	Sum
Triangle	60° each	180°
Square	90° each	360°
Trapezoid	60°, 120°	360°
Blue parallelogram	60°, 120°	360°
Tan rhombus	30°, 150°	360°
Hexagon	120° each	720°

Analyzing Angles

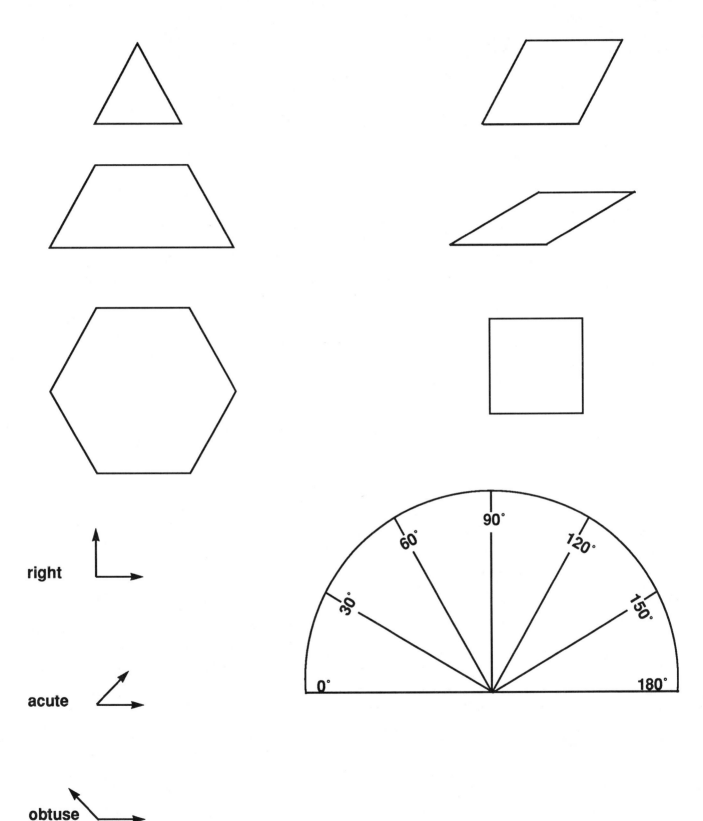

right

acute

obtuse

0°   30°   60°   90°   120°   150°   180°

Overhead Manipulatives in Action, 3–6
© 1992 Learning Resources, Inc.

Geoboards

Introduction

Using geoboards, students can learn about important geometric and measurement concepts in an informal, hands-on way. The activities in this unit will focus on exploring geometric shapes and relationships, transformations (translations, rotations, reflections), congruence, similarity, perimeter, and area. By maneuvering the rubber bands on the geoboard and recording their solutions from the geoboard onto a sheet of paper, students will improve their visual thinking and spatial reasoning skills. Due to the flexibility of the rubber bands, unlike drawing or constructing figures on a piece of paper, students can refine their problem-solving strategies and develop analytical reasoning without erasing or starting an exercise over again. Several geoboard forms (pages 66, 67, 68) and generic worksheets (pages 70, 72, 74, 76, 78) are available for students to record their solutions.

Geoboard Activities

Pages 69–70   Shapes, Sides, Corners
      71–72   Stretches and Shrinks
      73–74   Slides, Turns, Flips
      75–76   Exploring Perimeter
      77–78   Exploring Area

Getting Organized

Materials you will need:

◆ *Transparent Geoboard* (LER 152T) with rubber bands
◆ One transparency each of pages 66, 67, 68, 70, 72, 74, 76, 78
◆ Blank transparencies, overhead pens

Materials students will need:

◆ *Geoboard* (LER 152 Plastic) with rubber bands
◆ Copies of pages 66, 67, 68, 70, 72, 74, 76, 78
◆ Pencils, masking tape or small stickers

Note: Have several copies of pages 66, 67, and 68 available so that students can record multiple solutions for the various exercises.

Getting Started

Free Exploration. Distribute geoboards and rubber bands to students. (You might remind students about respect for others when working with the rubber bands.) Let students have some free exploration time with the geoboards. Display your transparent geoboard on the projector and ask students to describe the geoboard and its pegs. If students have formed shapes on their geoboards, ask them how the pegs are used in the shapes—to form corners and to form sides. Tell students to create a design on their geoboards and then record it on page 66. Students could make letters, numerals, animals, or other shapes.

Line Segments. Ask students to make straight line segments ("lines") on the geoboard with the rubber bands. Tell them to draw all the lines that they find on a copy of page 66. Define a linear unit as ●—● before asking the students to report on the possible lengths of each line. Ask:

How long is the shortest line? [1 unit]
How long is the longest non-diagonal line? [4 units]
Which line is the longest? [middle diagonal line]
How long is the longest line? [more than 4 units]

Geoboard

Overhead Manipulatives in Action, 3–6
© 1992 Learning Resources, Inc.

Geoboards

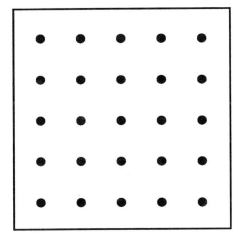

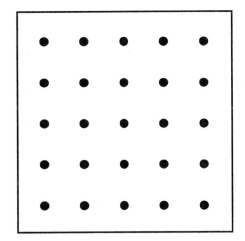

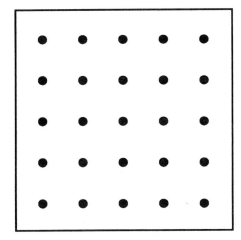

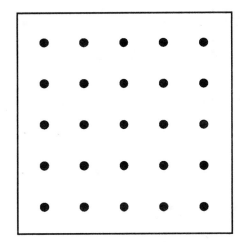

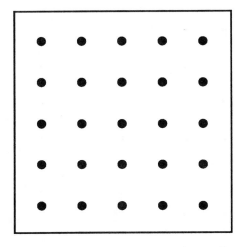

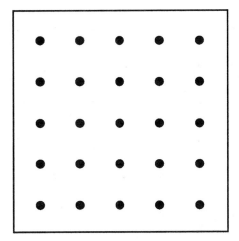

Dot Paper

Shapes, Sides, Corners

✓ Objectives

To copy shapes.
To make shapes.

Vocabulary

shape, side, corner

Materials

Transparent Geoboards, *Plastic Geoboards*, rubber bands, transparency of page 70, blank transparencies, overhead pens, student copies of pages 67 and 70, pencils

Warm-Up

Copy Shapes. Distribute geoboards and page 67. Display the transparent geoboard on the projector. Make a shape on the geoboard with the rubber bands. Ask students to copy the shape and then draw it on one of the small geoboards on page 67. Present the following six shapes: *triangle, square, rectangle, parallelogram, pentagon, hexagon.* Discuss the characteristics of each shape.

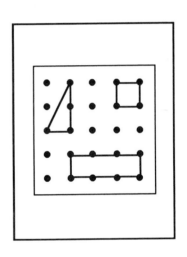

Activity

Making Shapes. Give each student a geoboard and three copies of page 70. Display the transparency of page 70 on the projector. Tell students to find four different shapes that touch 4 pegs. (Write 4 in the blank of the sentence at the top of the page.) Tell the students to draw the four shapes and record the number of sides and corners for each. Have the students fill in the other three copies of page 70 to find different shapes for 5 pegs and 6 pegs.

Practice

Since some students may have difficulty finding at least four different shapes for a given number of pegs, let them work in pairs or small groups. Observe students as they manipulate the rubber bands on the geoboard and as they record the shapes on page 70. If some students are having difficulty drawing straight lines, suggest that they use a ruler.

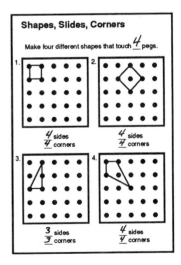

Wrap-Up

Discuss the three pages with students. Have them come to the projector to show their shapes that touch 4, 5, and 6 pegs.

For 4 pegs: Triangles; 3 sides, 3 corners. Different-sized squares and irregular-shaped quadrilaterals; 4 sides, 4 corners.

For 5 pegs: Triangles; 3 sides, 3 corners. Rhombus, irregular-shaped quadrilaterals; 4 sides, 4 corners. Pentagons; 5 sides, 5 corners.

For 6 pegs: Triangles; 3 sides, 3 corners. Rectangle, parallelograms, irregular-shaped quadrilaterals, trapezoids; 4 sides, 4 corners. Pentagons; 5 sides, 5 corners. Hexagons; 6 sides, 6 corners.

Shapes, Sides, Corners

Make four different shapes that touch _____ pegs.

1.

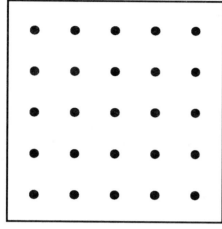

_____ sides

_____ corners

2.

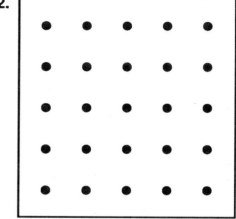

_____ sides

_____ corners

3.

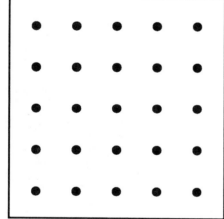

_____ sides

_____ corners

4.

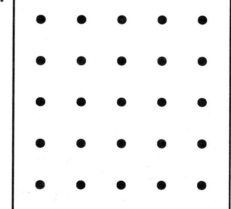

_____ sides

_____ corners

Overhead Manipulatives in Action, 3–6
© 1992 Learning Resources, Inc.

Stretches and Shrinks

 Objectives

To enlarge (stretch) a shape proportionately.
To decrease (shrink) a shape proportionately.
To learn about similar shapes.

Vocabulary

larger, smaller, similar

Materials

Transparent Geoboards, *Plastic Geoboards*, rubber bands, transparency of page
72, blank transparencies, overhead pens, student copies of page 72, pencils

Warm-Up

Similar Shapes. Show pairs of shapes on the geoboard at the projector. Ask how
they are the same and how they are different. For example:

- ◆ two squares, one touching 4 pegs and one touching 8 pegs;
- ◆ two right triangles, one touching 3 pegs and one touching 6 pegs;
- ◆ two rectangles, one touching 6 pegs and one touching 12 pegs.

Summarize this activity by showing students that a pair of *similar shapes* have
the same shape but are proportionately different in size.

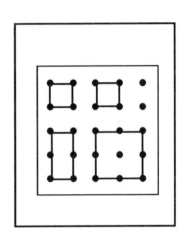

Activity

Stretches and Shrinks. Distribute a geoboard and page 72. Prepare the
transparency of page 72 with specific information (see the illustration at the
right). Ask students to copy your transparency by drawing the shapes on their
worksheets on the left side of each problem, circle either *larger* or *smaller*, and
write in the requested number in the blank. Work through the first problem on
the projector with a full-size geoboard. Show a square that touches 8 pegs and
ask the students to make it smaller so that it will only touch 4 pegs. Tell students
that the shapes must be the same and that only the size must be *proportionately
larger* or *smaller*.

Practice

Have students complete the other two problems on the page. Provide them with
additional copies of page 72 and encourage them to make their own pairs of
similar shapes.

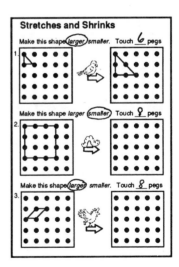

Wrap-Up

Discuss the shapes with students. Ask students whether they can make each
shape larger or smaller using a different number of pegs.

Stretches and Shrinks

Make this shape *larger smaller.*
(Choose one.)

Touch _____ pegs.

1.

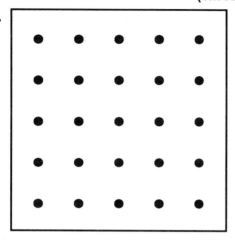

Make this shape *larger smaller.*
(Choose one.)

Touch _____ pegs.

2.

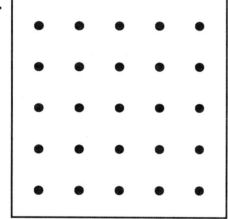

Make this shape *larger smaller.*
(Choose one.)

Touch _____ pegs.

3.

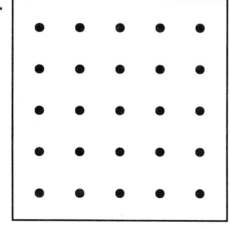

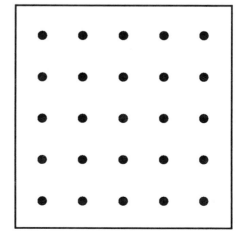

Geoboards

(72)

Overhead Manipulatives in Action, 3–6
© 1992 Learning Resources, Inc.

Slides, Turns, Flips

✔ **Objectives**

To show a translation (slide) of a shape.
To show a rotation (turn) of a shape.
To show a reflection (flip) of a shape.
To learn about congruent shapes.

Vocabulary

slide, turn, flip, congruent

Materials

Transparent Geoboards, Plastic Geoboards, rubber bands, transparencies of pages 66 and 74, blank transparencies, overhead pens, student copies of pages 66 and 74, pencils, masking tape or small stickers

Warm-Up

Congruent Shapes. Give each student a geoboard. Make a small shape on the transparent geoboard and display it on the projector. Direct students to form the shape and then make it again in another position on the geoboard. After doing a few shapes, explain to students that shapes are *congruent* if they have the same size and shape although their positions may vary.

Slide a Shape. Modify the activity above by asking students to form their shape "1 space right" or "2 spaces down" from the original shape. Distribute page 70 designating the shapes, circling "Slide ____" and writing in directions like "1 right" in the blank.

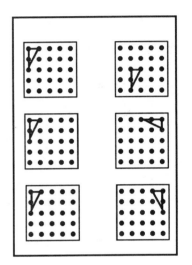

Activity

Turn a Shape. Give students a geoboard, page 66, 3 copies of page 74, and a piece of masking tape or a sticker. (Students should work with *Transparent Geoboards* if available.) Ask students to place the tape (or sticker) in the upper left-hand corner of their geoboard. Likewise, mark the geoboard on the projector with a marker. Form a rectangle on the geoboard and place it on the transparency of page 66. Note both are the same size. Draw the rectangle on page 66, then give the geoboard a quarter turn. Students should follow along with their geoboards and page 66. Place the geoboard in the original position and give it a half turn to see where the rectangle is positioned. Try other shapes with 90°, 180°, and 270° rotations.

Flip a Shape. To show a flip, pick up the geoboard and flip it over so that the pegs are on the bottom side of the pegboard. (Students should work with *Transparent Geoboards* if available.) Assign problems on page 74 focusing on the "Flip" portion of the directions.

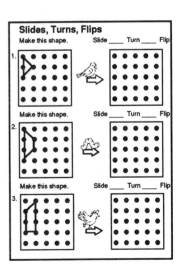

Practice

Have students record slides, flips, and turns on each copy of page 74.

Wrap-Up

Discuss the findings with students.

Extension Activity

Ask students to choose a shape and rotate it on page 66 to make a pattern.

Slides, Turns, Flips

Make this shape.

Slide _____ Turn _____ Flip

(Choose one.)

1.

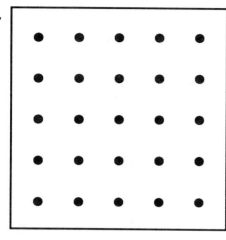

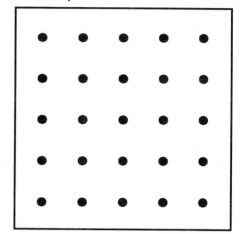

Make this shape.

Slide _____ Turn _____ Flip

(Choose one.)

2.

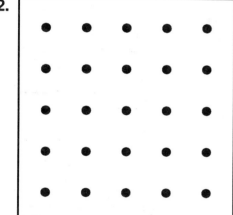

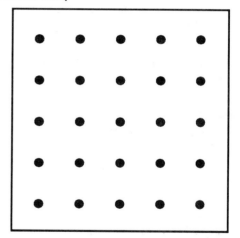

Make this shape.

Slide _____ Turn _____ Flip

(Choose one.)

3.

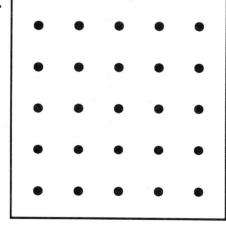

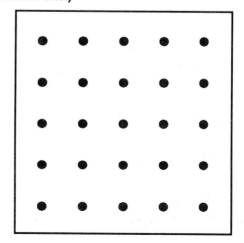

Overhead Manipulatives in Action, 3–6
© 1992 Learning Resources, Inc.

Exploring Perimeter

✓ Objectives

To find the perimeter of a shape.
To create a shape for a given perimeter.

Vocabulary

perimeter

Materials

Transparent Geoboards, *Plastic Geoboards*, rubber bands, transparency of pages 67 and 76, blank transparencies, overhead pens, student copies of pages 67 and 76, pencils

Warm-Up

Find the Perimeter. Distribute geoboards and page 67. Display the *Transparent Geoboard* on the projector and place a rubber band around two pegs to show 1 unit (●——●). Then stretch the rubber band to the length of 2, 3, and 4 units. Show students that when a rubber band is placed around two pegs that are diagonal on the geoboard, the length is more than 1 unit. Now show a 2 × 3-unit rectangle on the geoboard. Ask students to copy the rectangle on their geoboards and then find the *perimeter*, or *distance around*, the rectangle [10 units]. Ask them how they found the perimeter. Show various right-angled shapes (square, "L" or " T" shapes) on the geoboard. Have students replicate your shapes on their geoboards and record the shapes and their perimeters on page 67.

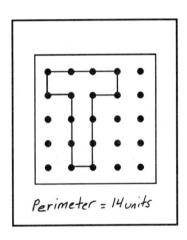

Perimeter = 14 units

Activity

Find a Shape for a Given Perimeter. Give each student a geoboard and page 76. Use the *Transparent Geoboard* on the projector. Ask a volunteer to show a shape that has a perimeter of 8 units. Then ask the class to find another shape with a perimeter of 8 units. Continue with other perimeters including some that are not possible, such as 5 units.

Practice

Have students find shapes that have perimeters of 10, 12, and 16 units, and record their shapes on page 76.

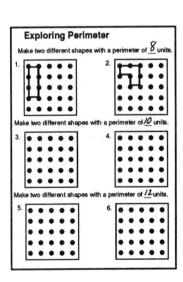

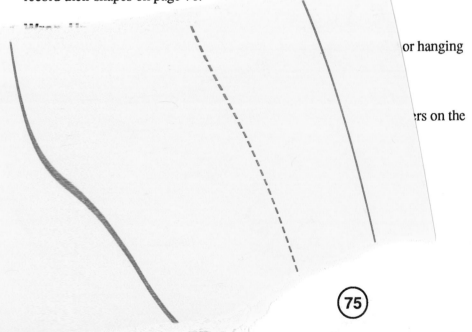

or hanging

ers on the

Geoboards

Exploring Perimeter

Make two different shapes with a perimeter of _____ units.

1.
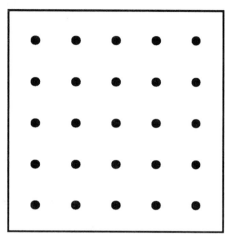

2.
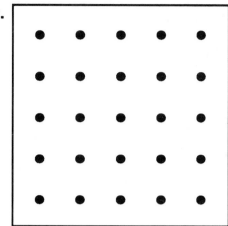

Make two different shapes with a perimeter of _____ units.

3.
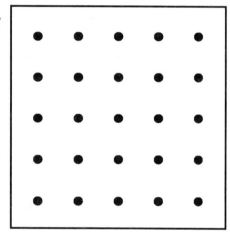

4.
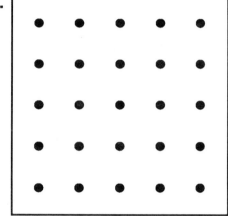

Make two different shapes with a perimeter of _____ units.

5.
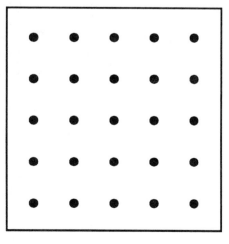

6.
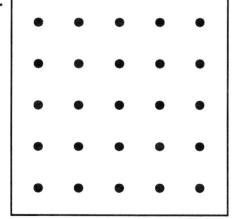

Overhead Manipulatives in Action, 3–6
© 1992 Learning Resources, Inc.

Exploring Area

 Objectives

To find the area of a shape.
To find a shape for a given area.

Vocabulary

area, square units

Materials

Transparent Geoboards, Plastic Geoboards, rubber bands, transparency of pages 67 and 78, blank transparencies, overhead pens; student copies of pages 67 and 78, pencils

Warm-Up

Find the Area. Give students geoboards and page 67. Display the *Transparent Geoboard* on the projector and place a rubber band around 4 pegs to make a small square. Tell students that 1 square unit is enclosed by the square that touches 4 pegs. Stretch the rubber band to make a rectangle that touches 6 pegs and tell them that 2 square units of area are enclosed in the rectangle. Continue with other examples asking students to give the area. Ask students to replicate your shapes on their geoboards, record the shapes and the area on page 67. Also try some shapes featuring 1/2 square units such as a trapezoid with 2 square units of area or a right triangle whose base is 4 units and its height is 4 units. [8 square units]

Activity

Find a Shape for a Given Area. Place the *Transparent Geoboard* on the projector and ask students to use their geoboards to find a shape with an area of 6 units. Hint that 1/2-unit squares are allowed. Give them an example of a 6 square unit shape such as a 2 × 3-unit rectangle.

Practice

Give students page 78. Display the transparency of page 78 on the projector and write the number 6 in the blank. Ask students to find six different shapes with an area of 6 on their geoboards and record the shapes.

Wrap-Up

Discuss the different shapes with students. Then ask them to find six shapes for another given area.

Extension Activity

Ask students to use their geoboards and find three ways to divide the geoboard in half, then find three ways to divide the geoboard into fourths. Students can record their work on page 67. Ask students if each part (halves or fourths) have the same area. [yes]

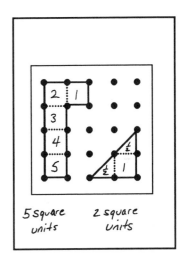

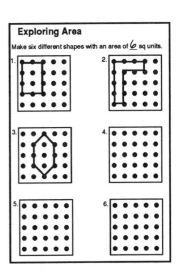

Exploring Area

Make six different shapes with an area of _____ square units.

1.

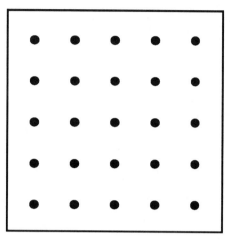

2.

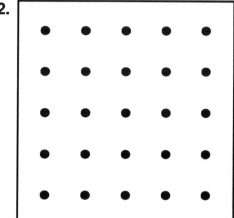

3.

4.

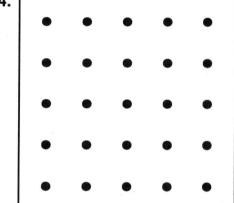

5.

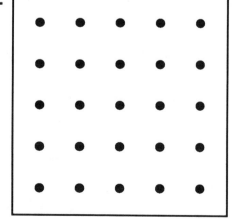

6.

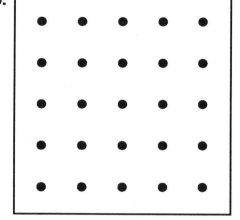

Overhead Manipulatives in Action, 3–6
© 1992 Learning Resources, Inc.

Fraction Squares

Introduction

Overhead Fraction Squares provide students with another hands-on manipulative that can be used to investigate fractional parts of a region, compare fractional numbers, and perform various operations. *Overhead Fraction Squares* are especially useful in demonstrating the connection between fraction, decimal, and percent representations of fractional numbers.

Fraction Squares Activities

Getting Organized

Materials you will need:

◆ *Overhead Fraction Squares* (LER 251)
◆ *Transparent Mini Metric Grids* (LER 311)
◆ *Overhead Base Ten Blocks* (LER 650)
◆ One transparency each of pages 84, 86, 88, 90, 92
◆ Blank transparencies, overhead pens

Materials students will need:

◆ Set of student-made Fraction Squares (pages 80, 81, 82)
◆ *Transparent Mini Metric Grids* (LER 311)
◆ *Base Ten Blocks* (plastic or wood)
◆ Copies of pages 80, 81, 82, 84, 86, 88, 90, 92
◆ Crayons or color markers, scissors, pencils, sheets of paper, 4" × 4" square sheets of paper

Getting Started

Distribute six 4" × 4" square sheets of paper to each student. Ask students to do the following:

◆ Color one whole square yellow.
◆ Fold one square in half. Color one-half green and label it 1/2.
◆ Fold one square in half, then in half again. Color one-fourth red and label it 1/4.
◆ Fold one square in half three times to give eight parts. Color one-eighth blue and label it 1/8.
◆ Fold one square into three equal parts. Color one-third purple and label it 1/3.
◆ Fold one square into thirds, then into sixths. Color one-sixth orange and label it 1/6.

This construction will give students insight into the set of *Overhead Fraction Squares*.

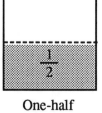

One-half
Green

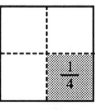

One-fourth
Red

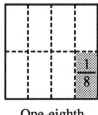

One-eighth
Blue

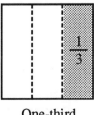

One-third
Purple

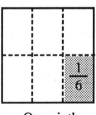

One-sixth
Orange

One and Hundredths

One

Hundredths

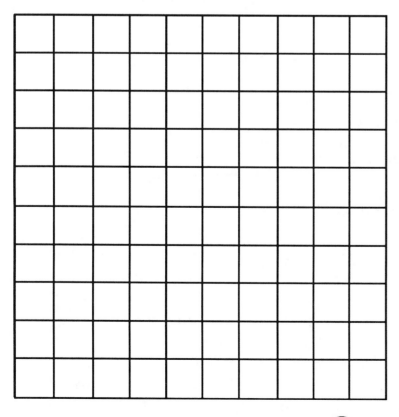

Fraction Squares
(80)

Overhead Manipulatives in Action, 3–6
© 1992 Learning Resources, Inc.

Halves, Fourths, and Eighths

Fourths

Half

Eighths

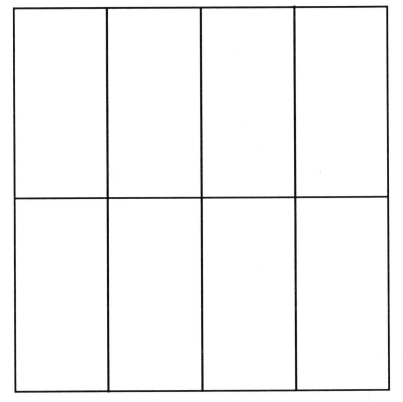

Half

Fraction Squares

Thirds and Sixths

Thirds

Sixths

Overhead Manipulatives in Action, 3–6
© 1992 Learning Resources, Inc.

Fraction Names

 Objective

To recognize and name fractions for halves, fourths, eighths, thirds, and sixths.

Vocabulary

fraction, half, third, fourth, sixth, eighth, numerator, denominator, unit fraction, proper fraction

Materials

Overhead Fraction Squares, transparency of page 84, overhead pens, 23 index cards; student copies of pages 80, 81, 82, and 84, pencils, crayons

Warm-Up

Have students color and cut out the Fraction Squares on pages 80, 81, and 82. [*Note*: Students will need these cutouts for all the lessons in this section.] Encourage them to look for relationships between the pieces. Students may discover that two greens (halves) make a yellow (whole), that a green (half) and two reds (fourths) make a whole, or that four blues (eighths) make a green (half).

Activity

Fraction Names. Have students take out their square fraction sets and distribute page 84. Then display the transparency of page 84 on the projector. Place two green pieces (halves) on the square as students follow along at their seats. Work with students to answer each question. Continue with four red pieces (fourths). Then model 1/4, 2/4, and 3/4 as you show students how to write each fraction. Follow the same procedure for eighths, thirds, and sixths. Each shaded section of their paper models represents a *unit fraction*. Several same-size pieces with a value less than one represents a *proper fraction*.

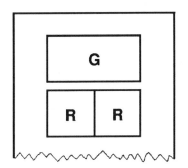

Practice

Write each of the following fractions on an index card: 1/2, 2/2, 1/3, 2/3, 3/3, 1/4, 2/4, 3/4, 4/4, 1/6, 2/6, 3/6, 4/6, 5/6, 6/6, 1/8, 2/8, 3/8, 4/8, 5/8, 6/8, 7/8, and 8/8. Shuffle the cards, place them face down in a deck, and ask each student to select a card. For each card, students draw the fraction on page 84, then answer the questions.

Wrap-Up

Have each student talk about the fraction selected. Display student work on the bulletin board.

Extension Activity

Ask students how they could find the unit fractions 1/16, 1/12, or 1/30 using 4" × 4" squares of paper. Also encourage them to show how proper fractions like 5/9 or 13/16 would look using 4" × 4" squares of paper. Students can paste their fraction models on page 84, then present their fractions to the class. Distribute copies of pages 80, 81, or 82 as needed.

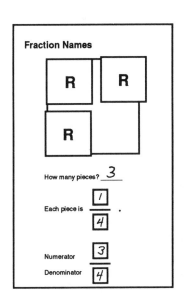

Fraction Names

How many pieces? _____

Each piece is ▢/▢ .

Numerator → ▢

Denominator → ▢

Overhead Manipulatives in Action, 3–6
© 1992 Learning Resources, Inc.

Comparing Fractions

 Objective

To compare fractional numbers using fraction squares.

Vocabulary

compare, equivalent, greater than, less than

Materials

Overhead Fraction Squares, transparency of page 86, blank transparencies, half sheet of paper, overhead pens; student-made Fraction Squares Set, student copies of page 86, pencils

Warm-Up

Play *Fraction Flash* with students. Place the transparency of page 86 on the projector and cover the lower half of it with a half sheet of paper. Tell students that you are going to show a fraction model to them for a few seconds, then turn off the projector. Ask students to write the fraction for each model they see. Try to display as many halves, thirds, fourths, sixths, and eighths as possible in a few minutes.

Activity

Comparing Fractions. Distribute page 86. Tell students to take out their Fraction Squares Set. Display the transparency of page 86 on the projector. Place a green (one-half) piece on the top square and a purple (one-third) piece on the bottom square. Ask the students to do the same and then to name the fractional parts. Then ask them which piece is *larger* and how they can prove it. Try another example showing two fraction pictures (3/6 and 1/2) that are *equivalent* to each other.

Practice

Give several copies of page 86 to each group of students. Ask students to work cooperatively in groups of three or four to find pairs of fractions either equivalent to each other or one larger than the other. One group could find all the fractional parts equivalent to 1/2, another group could find all fractional parts equivalent to 3/4, another group could find all fractional parts greater than 1/2, and so on.

Wrap-Up

Have each group present their fractional pictures (on page 86) to the class. Some students may wish to show their fractional comparisons on the projector using the *Overhead Fraction Squares* on the transparency of page 86.

Extension Activity

Challenge students to find all the ways to make the square fractional pieces equivalent to 1. This activity will give students an intuitive idea for adding with fractional numbers.

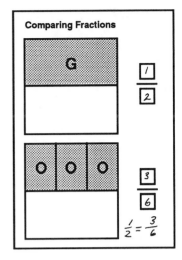

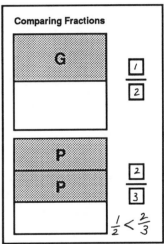

Extension Solutions:

1/2, 1/2
1/2, 1/4, 1/4
1/2, 1/4, 1/8, 1/8
1/2, 1/8, 1/8, 1/8, 1/8
1/4, 1/4, 1/4, 1/4
1/4, 1/4, 1/4, 1/8, 1/8
1/4, 1/4, 1/8, 1/8, 1/8, 1/8
1/4, 1/8, 1/8, 1/8, 1/8, 1/8, 1/8
1/8, 1/8, 1/8, 1/8, 1/8, 1/8, 1/8, 1/8
1/2, 1/3, 1/6
1/2, 1/6, 1/6, 1/6
1/3, 1/3, 1/3
1/3, 1/3, 1/6, 1/6
1/3, 1/6, 1/6, 1/6, 1/6
1/3, 1/6, 1/4, 1/8, 1/8
1/3, 1/6, 1/8, 1/8, 1/8, 1/8
1/6, 1/6, 1/6, 1/6, 1/6, 1/6
1/4, 1/4, 1/6, 1/6, 1/6
1/4, 1/8, 1/8, 1/6, 1/6, 1/6
1/8, 1/8, 1/8, 1/8, 1/6, 1/6, 1/6

Fraction Squares

Comparing Fractions

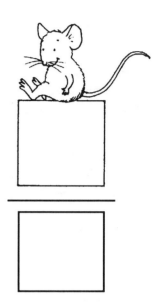

Overhead Manipulatives in Action, 3–6
© 1992 Learning Resources, Inc.

Adding Fractions

 Objective

To add fractions with like and unlike denominators.

Vocabulary
add, addend, sum, in all, altogether

Materials
Overhead Fraction Squares, transparency of page 88, blank transparencies, overhead pens; student-made Fraction Squares Set, student copies of page 88, pencils

Warm-Up
Adding Fractions with Like Denominators. Give students page 88. Display the transparency of page 88 on the projector. Ask students to place a red piece (1/4), then two more red pieces (2/4) on the square on their page. Ask, **How much of the square is covered with red pieces?** [3/4] **What addition equation can we write to show what we just modeled?** [1/4 + 2/4 = 3/4] Note: Frequently students will add both the numerator and denominator when adding fractions. Using fraction models will help students understand that when fourths are added to more fourths, the sum is fourths. Have students model and write other addition problems such as 2/8 + 3/8 = 5/8 and 1/6 + 2/6 = 3/6. Ask students if they can express some sums using only one fraction piece; for example, the sum of 3/6 (three orange pieces) can be expressed as 1/2 (one green piece).

Activity
Adding Fractions with Unlike Denominators. Present this problem to students: **What is the sum if you add 1/4 (red piece) and 1/2 (green piece)? Write the fraction number sentence below the square. 1/4 + 1/2 = ___. When we add fourths and fourths, we get fourths. When we add sixths and sixths, we get sixths. What do we get when we add fourths and halves? How much of the square is covered for 1/4 + 1/2?** [3/4] **Can you trade 1/2 for 2/4?** [yes] **Now we can write 1/4 + 2/4 = 3/4. Now try: 1/3 + 1/2 = ___.** [5/6]

Practice
Write 8 to 10 addition problems with fractions on the chalkboard and ask pairs of students to find the sums using their square fraction sets and page 88.

Wrap-Up
Ask volunteers to use the *Overhead Fraction Squares* and the projector to demonstrate how they found the sums.

Extension Activity
Challenge students to find sums of fractions such as 1/4 + 1/3. Ask students what happens when a paper folded in fourths is folded into thirds [twelfths]. Ask how finding the sum helps them.

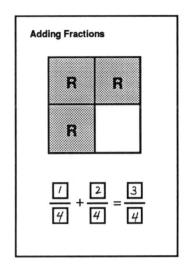

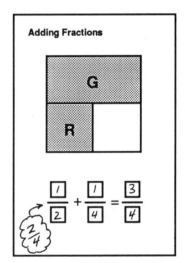

Try these problems:

1/6 + 1/2	3/8 + 1/2
1/6 + 3/6 = 4/6	3/8 + 4/8 = 7/8
or 2/3	
1/2 + 1/8	1/6 + 1/3
4/8 + 1/8 = 5/8	1/6 + 2/6 = 3/6
	or 1/2
1/3 + 1/2	1/4 + 1/8
2/6 + 3/6 = 5/6	2/8 + 1/8 = 3/8
2/8 + 3/4	2/3 + 2/6
2/8 + 6/8 = 8/8	4/6 + 2/6 = 6/6
or 1	or 1

Challenges:

1/4 + 1/3 [7/12]	1/6 + 1/4 [5/12]

Adding Fractions

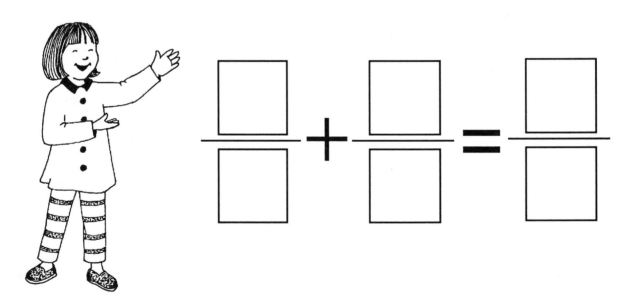

Overhead Manipulatives in Action, 3–6
© 1992 Learning Resources, Inc.

Fractions and Decimals

 Objective

To represent fractional numbers as fractions and decimals.

Vocabulary

hundredths, decimal

Materials

Overhead Fraction Squares, Transparent Mini Metric Grid, Overhead Base Ten Blocks, transparencies of pages 80 and 90, overhead pen; student-made Fraction Squares Set, *Base Ten Blocks*, student copies of pages 80 and 90, pencils

Warm-Up

Note: Students should have had some exposure to decimals and fractions before this activity. Distribute page 80 and *Base Ten Blocks*. Display the transparency of page 80 on the projector, or use a *Transparent Mini Metric Grid*. Place a hundreds block on the *one whole* square and tell students it represents one whole. Place a ones block on a *hundredths square* and tell students it represents one hundredth. Ask, **How many hundredths are in one whole?** [100] Write "1" next to the *one whole* square. Write the fraction "1/100" and the decimal "0.01" next to the *hundredths square*. Next, place a tens block on the *hundredths square*. Ask students to identify the fractional value. Write "1/10" and "0.1" next to the square. Ask: **How many hundredths are in 1/10?** [10] **Are 1/10 and 10/100 equivalent fractions?** [yes] Place five tens blocks on the square. Ask students to identify this amount as a fraction and decimal. [50/100, 0.50]

Activity

Fractions and Decimals. Distribute page 90. Place the transparency of page 90 on the projector. Place a green piece on each of the squares. Give the fraction name [1/2] and then find the decimal name [0.50]. Next, place a blue piece on each square. Give the name of the blue piece [1/8] and then ask the students to find the decimal name by counting the squares it covers on the *hundredths square*. [There are 10 whole squares and 5 half squares, or 12 1/2 squares covered in blue. The decimal name would be 0.125.]

Practice

Ask pairs of small groups of students to find the decimal names for all of the fraction square pieces as well as 1/5, 1/10, and 1/100.

Wrap-Up

Have students explain how they found the decimal names for the fraction square pieces, especially 1/3 and 1/6.

Extension Activity

Have students find decimal names for 2/3, 3/4, 3/8, 5/8, 7/8, 5/6, 2/5, and 7/10 based on the information they discovered in the activity above.

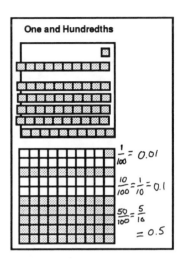

One and Hundredths

$$\frac{1}{100} = 0.01$$
$$\frac{10}{100} = \frac{1}{10} = 0.1$$
$$\frac{50}{100} = \frac{5}{10}$$
$$= 0.5$$

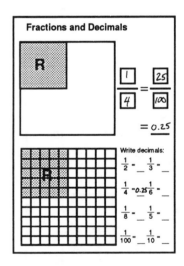

Fractions and Decimals

$$\frac{1}{4} = \frac{25}{100}$$
$$= 0.25$$

Write decimals:

$\frac{1}{2} =$ _ $\frac{1}{3} =$ _

$\frac{1}{4} = 0.25$ $\frac{1}{6} =$ _

$\frac{1}{8} =$ _ $\frac{1}{5} =$ _

$\frac{1}{100} =$ _ $\frac{1}{10} =$ _

Know these:
1/2 = 0.50 or 0.5
1/3 = 0.33*

1/4 = 0.25
1/6 = 0.17*

1/8 = 0.125
1/5 = 0.20 or 0.2

1/100 = 0.01
1/10 = 0.10 or 0.1

* Since 1/3 and 1/6 are repeating decimals, simply use decimals to the nearest hundredth.

Fractions and Decimals

$$\frac{\boxed{}}{\boxed{100}} = \frac{\boxed{}}{\boxed{100}}$$

$$= 0.\underline{}$$

Write the decimal.

$\dfrac{1}{2} = \underline{}$ $\dfrac{1}{3} = \underline{}$

$\dfrac{1}{4} = \underline{}$ $\dfrac{1}{6} = \underline{}$

$\dfrac{1}{8} = \underline{}$ $\dfrac{1}{5} = \underline{}$

$\dfrac{1}{100} = \underline{}$ $\dfrac{1}{10} = \underline{}$

Fraction Squares   (90)

Overhead Manipulatives in Action, 3–6
© 1992 Learning Resources, Inc.

Fractions and Percent

 Objective

To represent fractional numbers as fractions and percents.

Vocabulary

"per hundred," percent

Materials

Overhead Fraction Squares, Transparent Mini Metric Grids, transparencies of pages 80 and 92, blank transparencies, overhead pens; student-made Fraction Squares Set, student copies of pages 80 and 92, pencils

Warm-Up

Note: Students should have had some exposure to percent before this activity. Distribute page 80. Display a transparency of page 80 (or a *Transparent Mini Metric Grid*) on the projector. Place the yellow piece on the *one whole* square and ask students to give the number it represents. [1] Then ask students to identify how many squares are in the *hundredths* square. [100] Ask, **What fraction names this piece?** [100/100] **Is 1 the same as 100/100?** [yes] **Do you think 1 is the same as 100%?** [yes] **Why?** [1 is a whole thing and 100% is a whole thing] Review the following:

percent means "per hundred" or " □/100" or "___%"

Start again by placing a red fraction piece on each square on page 80. **What fractional part of the square is covered?** [1/4] **How many hundredths are covered?** [25/100] **25/100 is "25 per hundred" so, what percent is 25/100?** [25%] Write 1/4 = 25/100 = 25% next to the squares.

Activity

Fractions and Percents. Distribute copies of page 92. Place the transparency of page 92 on the projector. Place a purple piece on each square. Give the fraction name [1/3] and ask students to count the hundredths to find the percent equivalent to 1/3. [There are 30 whole squares and 10 thirds, or 33 1/3 tiny squares covered by the purple piece; approximately 33%] Except for half percents, such as for 1/8, round each percent to the nearest tenth. Try another example and then assign the problems shown on page 92. If students completed page 90, have them find corresponding percent names for each fraction square piece.

Practice

Ask pairs or small groups of students to find the percent names for all of the fraction square pieces as well as 1/5, 1/10, and 1/100.

Wrap-Up

Have students explain how they found the percent names for the fraction square pieces.

Extension Activity

Have students find percent equivalents for 2/3, 3/4, 3/8, 5/8, 7/8, 5/6, 2/5, and 7/10 based on the information they discovered in the activity above.

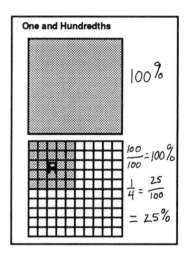

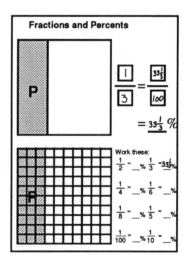

Know these:

1/2 = 50%	1/3 = 33%*
1/4 = 25%	1/6 = 17%*
1/8 = 12 1/2%	1/5 = 20%
1/100 = 1%	1/10 = 10%

* Since 1/3 and 1/6 are repeating decimals, simply round to the nearest whole percent.

Fractions and Percent

$$\frac{\boxed{}}{\boxed{}} = \frac{\boxed{}}{\boxed{100}}$$

$$= \underline{\quad\quad}\%$$

Write the percent.

$\dfrac{1}{2} = \underline{\quad}\%$ $\dfrac{1}{3} = \underline{\quad}\%$

$\dfrac{1}{4} = \underline{\quad}\%$ $\dfrac{1}{6} = \underline{\quad}\%$

$\dfrac{1}{8} = \underline{\quad}\%$ $\dfrac{1}{5} = \underline{\quad}\%$

$\dfrac{1}{100} = \underline{\quad}\%$ $\dfrac{1}{10} = \underline{\quad}\%$

Fraction Squares   (92)

Overhead Manipulatives in Action, 3–6
© 1992 Learning Resources, Inc.

Tangrams

Introduction

The tangram is an ancient Chinese puzzle consisting of a square divided into seven geometric shapes—two *large right triangles*, a *medium right triangle*, *two small right triangles*, a *square*, and a *parallelogram*. Countless geometric and pictorial arrangements can be made with the puzzle pieces. Visual and spatial awareness, in addition to mathematical concepts, are constantly enhanced when focusing on activities such as identifying and describing the pieces, combining the pieces to make other geometric shapes, exploring measurement concepts, and investigating fractional numbers. Without having an extensive background in measurement or geometry, students can use their logical reasoning skills to discover mathematical relationships between the pieces and to find multiple solutions to problems and puzzles.

Tangram Activities

 ## Getting Organized

Materials you will need:

◆ *Tangrams for the Overhead* (LER 418)
◆ *Transparent Inch Grids* (LER 309)
◆ *Transparent Centimeter Grids* (LER 310)
◆ *Transparent Mini Metric Grids* (LER 311)
◆ One transparency each of pages 98, 100, 102, 104, 106
◆ Blank transparencies, overhead pens

Materials students will need:

◆ *Tangrams* (LER 417)
◆ *Transparent Inch Grids* (LER 309)
◆ *Transparent Centimeter Grids* (LER 310)
◆ *Transparent Mini Metric Grids* (LER 311)
◆ Copies of pages 94, 95, 96, 98, 100, 102, 104, 106
◆ Crayons or color markers, scissors, pencils, sheets of paper, 4" × 4" squares of colored paper

 ## Getting Started

For students who have not had opportunities to work with the tangram previously, permit them to freely explore with the tangram pieces before you give a formal introduction to the pieces. Observe students as they form "tangram pictures" and listen carefully to the language used to describe each tangram piece.

Students who have previously worked with tangrams can construct the tangram puzzle from a 4-inch square piece of paper. Give them the model (page 94), and provide them with 4-inch squares of colored paper and scissors. Direct them to fold before cutting out the pieces. You may give the hint that there may be more folds than cuts in order to figure out the size of some pieces. Listen for mathematical language such as "fold in half diagonally" or "fold in half along the height and then fold down to match a vertex to the midpoint of the opposite side" as the students make their tangram puzzles.

The Tangram

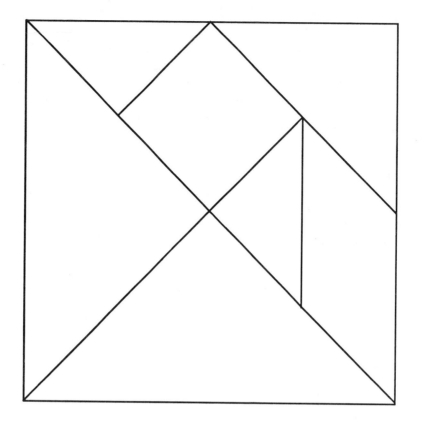

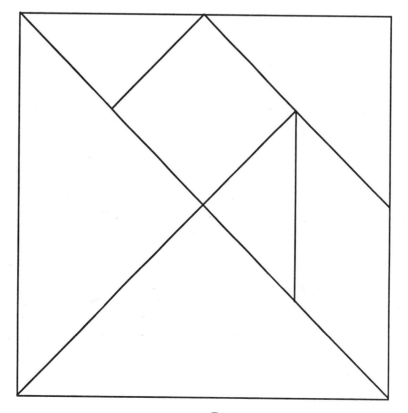

Overhead Manipulatives in Action, 3–6
© 1992 Learning Resources, Inc.

Inch Grid

Centimeter Grid

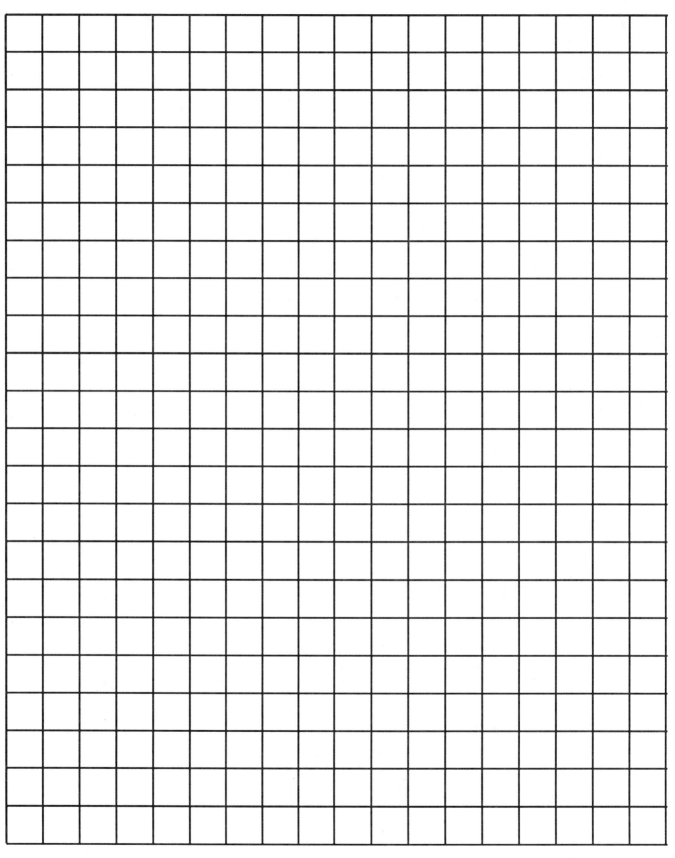

Overhead Manipulatives in Action, 3–6
© 1992 Learning Resources, Inc.

Tangram Shapes

 Objectives

To identify and describe the tangram pieces.
To make a tangram shape using other tangram pieces.

Vocabulary
tangram, triangle, square, parallelogram

Materials
Tangrams for the Overhead, transparency of page 98, blank transparencies, overhead pens; *Tangrams*, student copies of page 98, pencils

Warm-Up
Distribute tangrams and page 98. Display the transparency of page 98 on the projector. Ask students to match a tangram piece to each of the figures shown on the page. The remaining two pieces may be placed at the bottom of the page. Ask about the tangram pieces: **How many pieces?** [7] **How many shapes?** [3] **What are the shapes?** [triangle, square, parallelogram] **Can you say three things about each shape?** [mention sides, angles, size, etc.]

You may wish to have each student write a very concise descriptive sentence about each tangram piece, then share their sentences with the class. Depending on grade and ability level, the descriptions may range from general statements such as "A square has four sides and four corners." to "The large triangle contains a right angle. Since two of its three sides are the same length, it is an *isosceles right triangle*." Some students might also mention that the smaller angles in the triangles are 45° each and the angles of the parallelogram are 45° and 135°.

Activity
Tangram Shapes. Display page 98 on the projector and place the small triangle in its outline. Ask students how its size and shape compare to the other two triangles. **How many small triangles could fit on the medium triangle?** [2] **On the large triangle?** [4] **On the square?** [2] **On the parallelogram?** [2] **Try it.** Continue asking questions about other tangram shapes and their relation to each other.

Practice
Ask students to do the following tasks:
- ♦ **How many different ways can you cover the large triangle?**
- ♦ **What shape can you make using the two large triangles?**
- ♦ **What shape can you make using the two small triangles?**

Wrap-Up
Have students show and explain their solutions to the practice problems above.

Extension Activity
Ask students to describe a tangram piece in terms of the other tangram pieces. For example: "The medium triangle is twice as large as the small triangle." or "The medium triangle is only half as large as the large triangle."

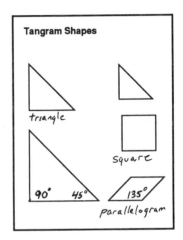

Tangram Shapes

triangle

square

90° 45° 135°

parallelogram

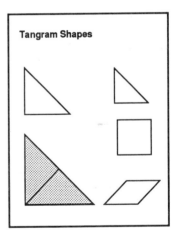

Tangram Shapes

Practice solutions:
Large triangle:
2 small triangles, 1 medium
  triangle
2 small triangles,
  1 parallelogram
2 small triangles, 1 square
4 small triangles

2 large triangles:
a large square,
a large parallelogram,
a larger right triangle

2 small triangles:
a small square,
a small parallelogram,
a larger right triangle

Tangram Shapes

Overhead Manipulatives in Action, 3–6
© 1992 Learning Resources, Inc.

Making Other Shapes

Objective
To make other geometric shapes with tangram pieces.

Vocabulary
trapezoid, rectangle, pentagon, hexagon

Materials
Tangrams for the Overhead, transparency of page 100, blank transparencies, overhead pens; *Tangrams*, student copies of page 100, paper, pencils

Warm-Up
Give students tangrams and paper. Ask them to use all the tangram pieces to make a large triangle and then a large parallelogram. After students find the solutions, have them trace the triangle and the parallelogram on paper and also show the interior lines for each figure.

Activity
Making Other Shapes. Distribute two copies of page 100 and tangrams to each student. Discuss the words *rectangle, trapezoid, pentagon,* and *hexagon.* On one copy of page 100, ask students to draw a simple sketch of each of the geometric shapes and to write a short description about each shape. You may wish to brainstorm with students before they do any writing by listing key words or phrases under each shape name. For example, for rectangle, the phrases *right angles, four sides, parallel sides, pairs of equal sides,* would be appropriate.

Practice
Using the other copy of page 100, ask students to find at least one way to make each geometric shape using some or all of the tangram pieces, trace the shape, and fill in the interior lines. Some students may request more copies of page 100 if they have found more than one solution for each shape.

Wrap-Up
Ask volunteers to display their solutions for each shape on the projector. Display students' work on the bulletin board.

Extension Activity
Small cooperative groups of students may wish to produce tangram books, each focusing on a particular theme such as the letters of the alphabet, numerals, animals, vehicles, or people.

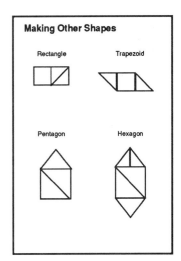

Making Other Shapes

Rectangle

Trapezoid

Pentagon

Hexagon

Overhead Manipulatives in Action, 3–6
© 1992 Learning Resources, Inc.

Exploring Area

 Objectives

To find the area of each tangram piece and the tangram puzzle.
To find the area of tangram shapes.

Vocabulary

area, square units, inch(es)

Materials

Tangrams for the Overhead, Transparent Inch Grids (or a transparency of page 95), transparency of page 102, blank transparencies, overhead pens; *Tangrams*, student copies of pages 95 and 102, crayons, pencils

Warm-Up

Area of Shapes. Distribute page 95. Display a *Transparent Inch Grid* or a transparency of page 95 on the projector. Draw a 2" × 3" rectangle on the grid. Ask students to find the area [6 sq in.]. Next draw a 3" × 3" square [area 9 sq in.] and a right triangle with a height of 3 inches and a base of 6 inches [area 9 sq in.] and ask students to give the area. Ask students to draw and find the area of some irregular shapes.

Activity 1

Area of Each Tangram Piece. Distribute page 102 and tangrams. Display the transparency of page 102 on the projector and a small triangle in its outline. Ask students to estimate the area of the shape, then place it on the inch grid. Encourage students to try different positions so they can find the exact area of the triangle. [1 sq in.] Ask, **If the small triangle has an area of 1 square inch, what do you think the area of the medium triangle would be?** [2 sq in.] **What is the area of the large triangle?** [4 sq in.] **The square?** [2 sq in.] **The parallelogram?** [2 sq in.]

Activity 2

Area of the Tangram. Ask students to place the five pieces on the inch grid. Ask, **How many square inches are covered?** [11 sq in.] **Place the remaining two tangram pieces on the inch grid. What is the area of the tangram?** [16 sq in.] **Does the area of the tangram puzzle ever change no matter what kind of shape is made with all seven pieces?** [No.] **Why or why not?**

Practice

Ask students to create seven-piece tangram shapes on page 95 or on the *Transparent Inch Grids*. Have them verify whether the area ever changes when the shape changes.

Wrap-Up

Ask students to present their tangram creations to the class. Have students give the area of each shape.

Extension Activity

Students can find the area of the tangram and each of its pieces in centimeters using page 96.

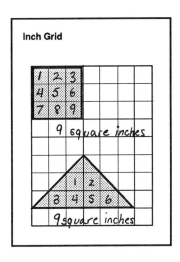

Inch Grid

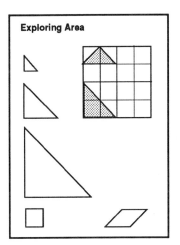

Exploring Area

Exploring Area

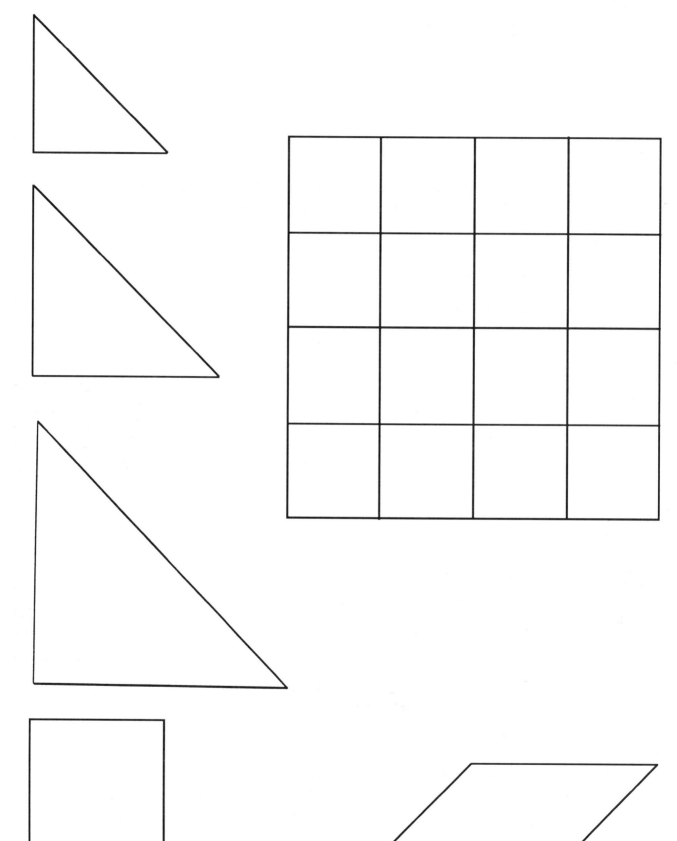

Overhead Manipulatives in Action, 3–6
© 1992 Learning Resources, Inc.

Exploring Perimeter

 Objectives

To find the perimeter of each tangram piece.
To find the perimeter of the tangram puzzle.
To find the perimeter of tangram shapes.

Vocabulary

perimeter, centimeters

Materials

Tangrams for the Overhead, Transparent Centimeter Grids (or a transparency of page 96), *Transparent Mini Metric Grids*, transparency of page 104, blank transparencies, overhead pens; *Tangrams*, student copies of pages 96 and 104, crayons, pencils

Warm-Up

Perimeter of Shapes. Distribute page 96. Display a *Transparent Centimeter Grid* or a transparency of page 96 on the projector. Draw a 2 × 3 cm rectangle on the grid. Ask students to find the perimeter (distance around a shape) and describe how they found it [10 cm]. Next, draw a 5 × 5 cm square [20 cm] and an isosceles triangle with a height of 8 cm and a base of 4 cm [about 21 cm]. *Note:* To help students understand that the measure of the diagonal is longer than the measure of the side of a square, have them use a centimeter ruler to measure each. Students can use estimation to find perimeters of triangles and irregular shapes.

Activity 1

Perimeter of Each Tangram Piece. Distribute page 104 and tangrams. Display the transparency of page 104 on the projector and a small triangle in its outline. Show students how to place the triangle on the grid, then try different positions so they can find the exact perimeter. [The sides measure 3.5 cm, 3.5 cm, and 5 cm for a total of 12 cm]. Find the perimeter for the remaining pieces.

Activity 2

Perimeter of the Tangram. Ask students to use all seven pieces to form a square on the centimeter grid, then find the perimeter. [40 cm] Ask, **If you create other shapes with all seven tangram pieces, will the perimeter change? Why or why not?** [The perimeter will vary depending on the figure that is formed.]

Practice

Ask students to create seven-piece tangram shapes on copies of page 96 or on the *Transparent Centimeter Grids*, then find the perimeter of each shape.

Wrap-Up

Ask students to present their tangram figures to the class. Have students give the perimeter of each figure.

Extension Activity

Students can find the perimeter of the tangram, each of its pieces, and various tangram shapes in inches using the *Transparent Inch Grids* or copies of page 95.

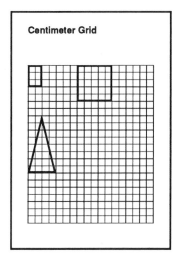

Centimeter Grid

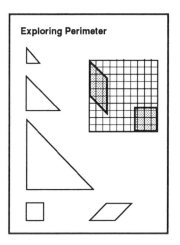

Exploring Perimeter

Exploring Perimeter

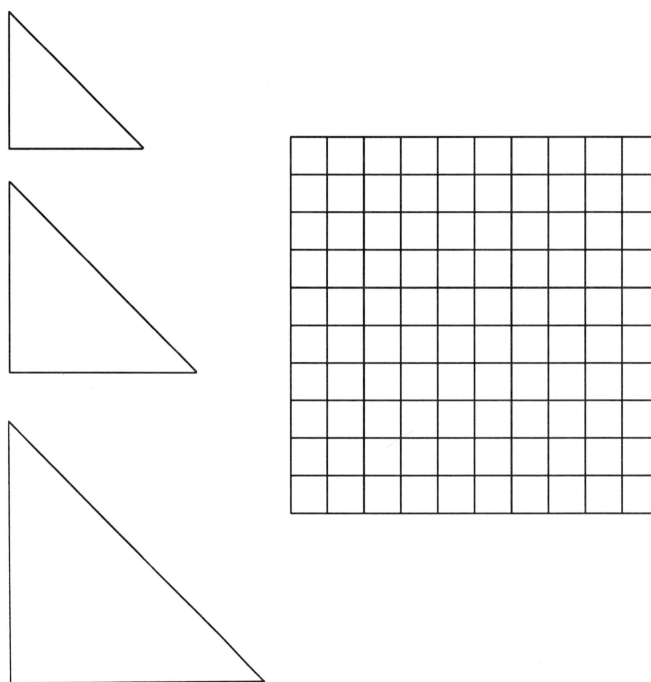

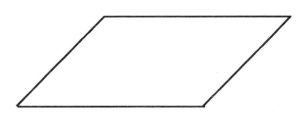

Overhead Manipulatives in Action, 3–6
© 1992 Learning Resources, Inc.

Tangram Fractions

✓ Objective

To identify fractional parts of the tangram.

Vocabulary

fraction

Materials

Tangrams for the Overhead, (Transparent Mini Metric Grids), transparencies of page 106, blank transparencies, overhead pens; *Tangrams*, student copies of page 106, 4" × 4" square pieces of colored paper, scissors, pencils

Warm-Up

Give each student page 106, a 4" × 4" square piece of paper, and a pair of scissors. Ask them to follow these directions to find fractional parts of the tangram: **Fold the square in half diagonally and then cut along the diagonal line. What fraction is each part?** [1/2] **Label one of the halves "1/2." Next, fold and cut the other half of the square. What part of the square is each part?** [1/4] **Label one of the parts "1/4." Next, fold and cut the other one-fourth in half. What part of the square is each part?** [1/8] **Label one of these parts "1/8." Finally, fold and cut the remaining piece in half. What part of the square is each piece?** [1/16]. **Label each part "1/16."** Each student should have 1/2, 1/4, 1/8, and two 1/16 pieces covering the square and should be ready for the activity below.

Activity

Tangram Fractions. Have students match the cutouts with the three tangram triangles and label the triangles accordingly on page 106 [1/16, 1/8, 1/4]. Ask students how they can use the information they know to find the fractional value of these tangram pieces: square and parallelogram. [Two small triangles, value of 1/16 each, cover the square or parallelogram. The value for these pieces is 1/16 + 1/16, or 1/8.] Then have students put their cutouts away as you distribute tangrams. Several activities can be done using fractional values of tangram pieces—finding equivalent fractions, adding fractions, and subtracting fractions. A sample problem in given for each fraction task in the *Practice* section.

Practice

Equivalent Fractions. Ask, **Which tangram pieces can show the fraction 1/4?**
Adding Fractions. Ask, **What fraction of the square is covered using a large triangle and a parallelogram?**
Subtracting Fractions. Put a large triangle, a medium triangle, and the parallelogram on the square and then take away 1/16. Ask, **What fractional part of the tangram pieces is left?** Prepare other problems for students or have them write problems to share with a partner.

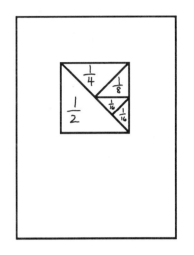

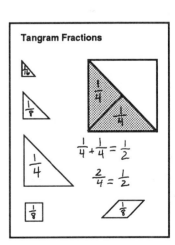

Wrap-Up

Have students display problems and their solutions to the class.

Extension Activity

Place the *Transparent Mini Metric Grid* over the square on page 106 and have students find the decimal and/or percent equivalents for each tangram piece.

Tangram Fractions

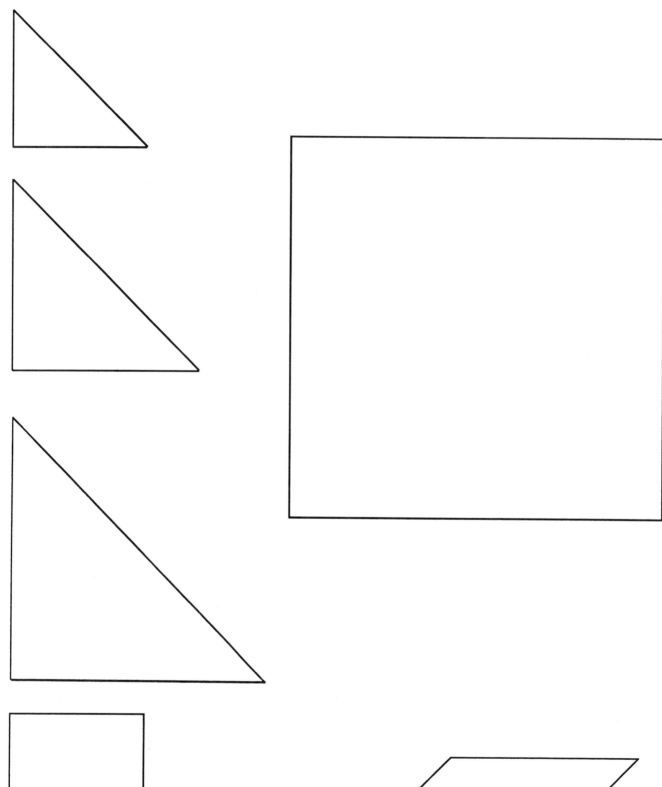

Overhead Manipulatives in Action, 3–6
© 1992 Learning Resources, Inc.

Rainbow Fraction Tiles

Introduction

Overhead Rainbow Fraction Tiles are ideal for demonstrating fractional relationships between 1, 1/2, 1/4, 1/8, 1/3, 1/6, 1/12, 1 /5, and 1/10 and the operations of addition, subtraction, multiplication, division. The 51 proportionally-sized fraction tiles are color-coded in nine colors to help students keep track of the fractional parts. Since these fraction tiles have the attribute of length, they may also be used to bridge the gap between fraction manipulatives and number lines exhibiting fractional increments.

Rainbow Fraction Tile Activities

Getting Organized

Materials you will need:

◆ *Overhead Rainbow Fraction Tiles* (LER 616)
◆ One transparency each of pages 112, 114, 116, 118, 120 and the number lines on page 110
◆ Blank transparencies, overhead pens

Materials students will need:

◆ *Rainbow Fraction Tiles* (LER 615)
◆ *Coin Set* (LER 101; 95–99)
◆ Copies of pages 108, 109, 110, 112, 114, 116, 118, 120
◆ Crayons or color markers, scissors, pencils, 8" × 1" strips of paper

Getting Started

Give four 8" × 1" strips of paper to each student. Ask students to do the following:

◆ Label one of the strips "1."
◆ Fold the second strip in half. **What fraction is each part?** [1/2] **Label each part 1/2.**
◆ Fold the third strip in half, then in half again. **What fraction is each part?** [1/4] **Label each part 1/4.**
◆ Fold the last strip in half three times. **What fraction is each part?** [1/8] **Label each part 1/8.**

This folding activity will give students insight into the *Rainbow Fraction Tiles* before they use them.

Distribute sets of *Rainbow Fraction Tiles*. Have students compare their folded fraction strips with the fraction tiles. Give students five additional paper strips to complete the folding activity to find thirds, sixths, twelfths, fifths, and tenths, then compare them to the fraction tiles. Have students label and discuss the *unit fractions*. Also identify *proper fractions* by having students cover the "1" tile or paper strip with other fraction tiles. For example, to show 3/4, cover a whole strip with three 1/4 tiles.

One, Halves, Fourths, Eighths

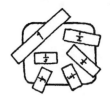

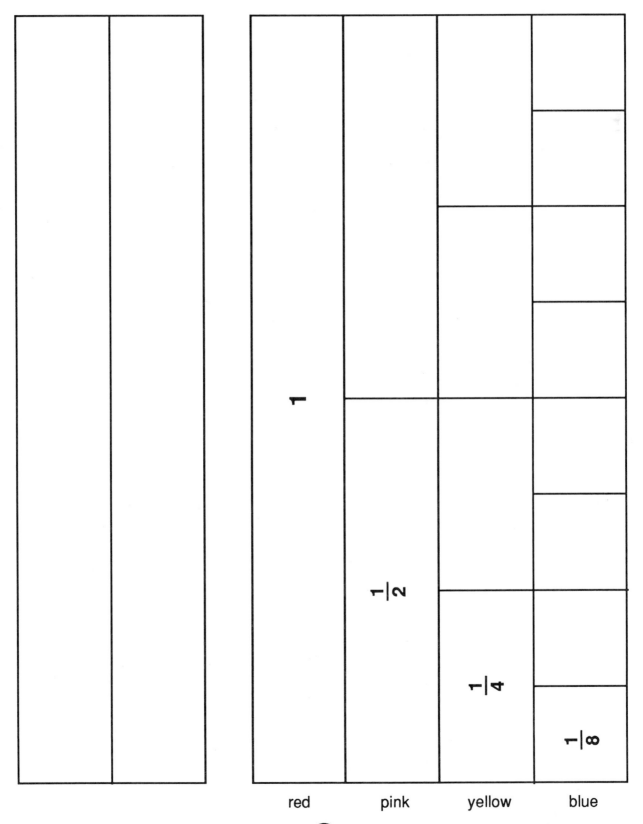

red   pink   yellow   blue

Rainbow Fraction Tiles

Overhead Manipulatives in Action, 3–6
© 1992 Learning Resources, Inc.

One, Thirds, Sixths, Twelfths

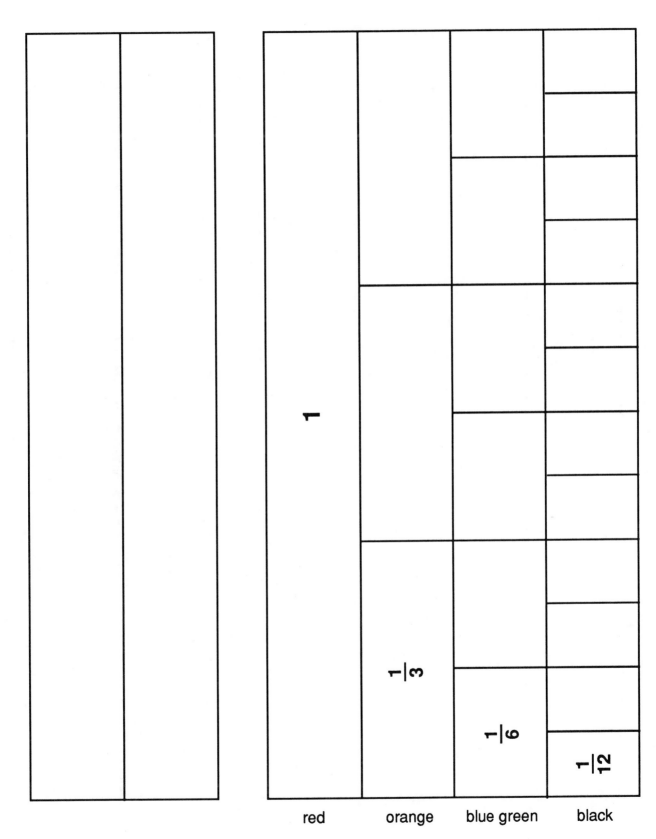

1

$\dfrac{1}{3}$

$\dfrac{1}{6}$

$\dfrac{1}{12}$

red   orange   blue green   black

Overhead Manipulatives in Action, 3–6
© 1992 Learning Resources, Inc.

Rainbow Fraction Tiles

One, Fifths, Tenths

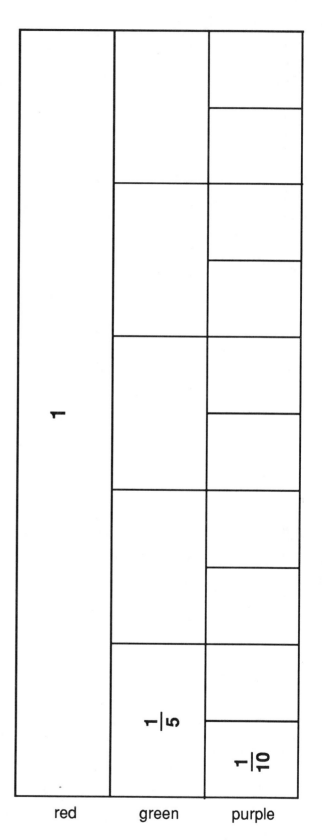

red   green   purple

Overhead Manipulatives in Action, 3–6
© 1992 Learning Resources, Inc.

Comparing Fractions

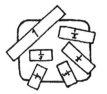

 Objectives

To compare fractions.
To find equivalent fractions.
To find lowest-terms fractions.

Vocabulary

fraction, equivalent, less than, greater than

Materials

Overhead Rainbow Fraction Tiles, transparency of pages 110 and 112, blank transparencies, overhead pens; *Rainbow Fraction Tiles*, student copies of number lines on pages 110 and 112, pencils

Warm-Up

Compare Fractions. Distribute copies of page 112 and *Rainbow Fraction Tiles* to students. (*Note:* The fraction tile chart in the upper left-hand corner of page 112 is a quick reference for students working with the tiles.) Display the transparency of page 112 on the projector. Write the fractions 1/2 and 1/3 in the fraction boxes and then place the corresponding *Overhead Rainbow Fraction Tiles* in the two unit strips below. Visually, the students should see that 1/2 is greater than 1/3. Place the appropriate symbol between the two fractions [1/2 > 1/3]. Try other pairs of fractions such as 5/8 and 7/12 or 3/4 and 6/8.

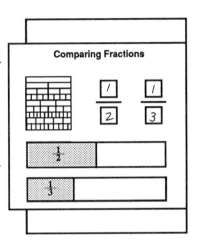

Activity 1

Finding Equivalent Fractions. Place the 1/2-fraction tile on the top strip and ask students to place other fraction tiles to make the same length in the bottom strip. [2/4, 3/6, 4/8, 5/10, 6/12] Try this exercise for the fractions 1/3, 1/4, 1/8, 1/6 and then for such fractions as 3/4, 2/3, and 4/5. Summarize each exercise by writing the equivalent fractions in the fraction boxes, such as 1/2 = 3/6.

Activity 2

Find Lowest-Terms Fractions. Place 3/6 on the top strip and ask students to find an equivalent fraction tile. Tell students that finding equivalent fractions and lowest-terms fractions is similar to making "trades" to represent the same value.

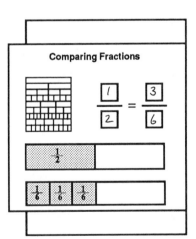

Practice

Ask students to use their *Rainbow Fraction Tiles* to find as many pairs of equivalent fractions as they can and record them. Make a class list of all the pairs of equivalent fractions.

Wrap-Up

Ask students to share their findings with the class, and tell how their findings relate to the fraction chart on page 112.

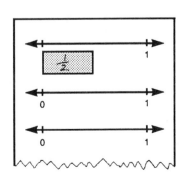

Extension Activity

Relate the *Rainbow Fraction Tiles* to the number line by placing the tiles next to a number line and marking the fraction increments. Three number lines are provided on page 110. Students can make number lines in 1/2's, 1/3's, and 1/5's, or use only one number line to show all the fraction increments.

Comparing Fractions

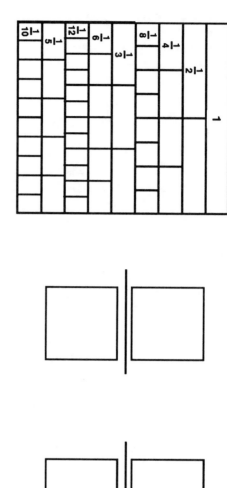

(112)

Adding Fractions

Objectives
To add fractions with like denominators.
To add fractions with unlike denominators.

Vocabulary
add, sum, like, unlike, numerator, denominator

Materials
Overhead Rainbow Fraction Tiles, transparency of page 114, blank transparencies, overhead pens; *Rainbow Fraction Tiles*, student copies of page 114, pencils

Warm-Up
Adding Fractions with Like Denominators. Have students work in pairs or small cooperative groups. Distribute page 114 and *Rainbow Fraction Tiles*, then display the transparency of page 114 on the projector. Demonstrate addition problems using like denominators. Start with pairs of fractions whose sums do not need simplifying, then move to those that do. Try this sequence of problems:

1/3 + 1/3 = 2/3	2/5 + 2/5 = 4/5	1/6 + 4/6 = 5/6
3/8 + 2/8 = 5/8	1/3 + 2/3 = 3/3 = 1	3/5 + 4/5 = 7/5 = 1 2/5

Model each addition using the *Overhead Rainbow Fraction Tiles*. Ask students to write the addition equation and simplest name for each sum. Conclude the lesson with some practice problems and a *Wrap-Up*, or continue to add fractions with unlike denominators.

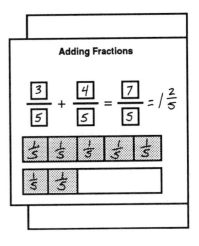

Activity
Adding Fractions with Unlike Denominators. Ask pairs or small groups of students to use the fraction tiles with page 114. Demonstrate a similar sequence of problems as students follow along:

1/4 + 1/2 = 1/4 + **2/4** = 3/4	5/12 + 1/3 = 5/12 + **4/12** = 9/12 = 3/4
5/6 + 1/3 = 5/6 + **2/6** = 7/6 = 1 1/6	2/3 + 5/6 = **4/6** + 5/6 = 9/6 = 1 3/6 = 1 1/2

As you display fraction tiles for each addition problem, remind students that equivalent fractions must be used (trades made) in order to find the sum, and then later to express the sum as the lowest-terms fraction or mixed number.

Practice
Have students make up and solve problems using the fraction tiles.

Wrap-Up
Discuss students' addition problems. Some students may wish to show their problems on the projector.

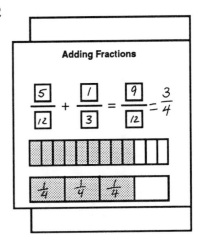

Extension Activity
Have students work in small groups to find sums of three or four fractions. *Note*: Students may have to make their own fraction tiles for 1/24's or 1/18's or 1/20's to solve problems such as 2/3 + 1/8.

Adding Fractions

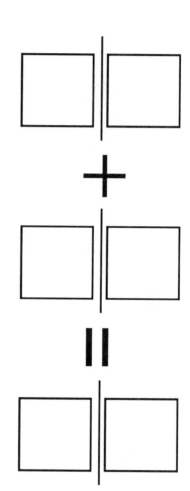

Overhead Manipulatives in Action, 3–6
© 1992 Learning Resources, Inc.

Subtracting Fractions

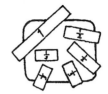

 Objectives

To subtract fractions with like denominators.
To subtract fractions with unlike denominators.

Vocabulary
subtract, difference

Materials
Overhead Rainbow Fraction Tiles, transparency of page 116, blank transparencies, overhead pens; *Rainbow Fraction Tiles*, student copies of page 116, pencils

Warm-Up
Subtracting Fractions with Like Denominators. Have students work in pairs or small cooperative groups. Distribute page 116 and *Rainbow Fraction Tiles*. Display the transparency of page 116 on the projector. Demonstrate subtraction problems using like denominators. Try a sequence of problems like this:

2/3 – 1/3 = 1/3   5/6 – 3/6 = 2/6 = 1/3
1 – 5/8 = **8/8** – 5/8 = 3/8   1 2/5 – 3/5 = **7/5** – 3/5 = 4/5

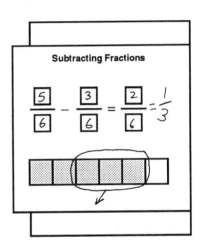

Model each subtraction problem using the *Overhead Rainbow Fraction Tiles*. Ask students to write the subtraction equation and simplest name for each difference. Conclude the lesson with some practice problems and a *Wrap-Up*, or continue to subtract fractions with unlike denominators.

Activity
Subtracting Fractions with Unlike Denominators. Ask pairs or small groups of students to use the fraction tiles with page 116. Demonstrate a similar sequence of problems as the students follow along:

3/4 – 1/2 = 3/4 – **2/4** = 1/4   2/3 – 1/6 = **4/6** – 1/6 = 3/6 = 1/2
1/2 – 3/8 = **4/8** – 3/8 = 1/8   1/3 – 1/4 = **4/12** – **3/12** = 1/12

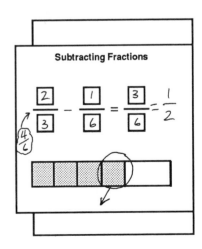

As you display fraction tiles for each subtraction problem, remind students that equivalent fractions must be used (trades made) in order to find the difference and then later to express the difference as the lowest-terms fraction.

Practice
Have students make up and solve problems using the fraction tiles.

Wrap-Up
Discuss students' subtraction problems. Some students may wish to show their problems on the projector.

Extension Activity
Challenge students to find differences to problems such as 2/3 – 1/8 [13/24]. Students will have to make their own fraction tiles for 1/24's.

Subtracting Fractions

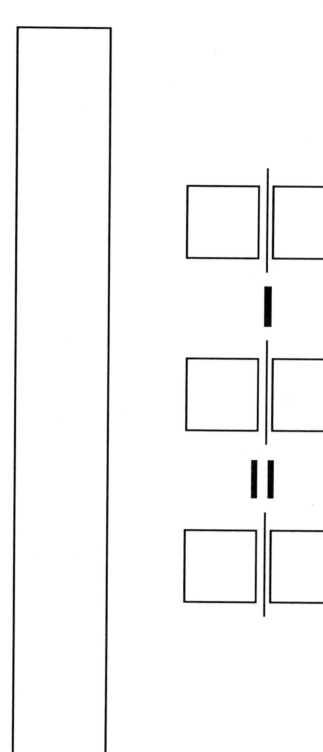

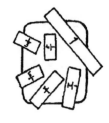

Overhead Manipulatives in Action, 3–6
© 1992 Learning Resources, Inc.

Multiplying Fractions

 Objectives

To multiply a fraction by a whole number.
To multiply a fraction by another fraction.

Vocabulary
multiply, product, mixed number

Materials
Overhead Rainbow Fraction Tiles, Overhead Coins, transparency of page 118, blank transparencies, overhead pens; *Rainbow Fraction Tiles*, play money coins, student copies of page 118, pencils

Warm-Up
Display coins on the projector and give students play money coins. Use these manipulatives to help students understand how to find a whole number times a fractional part and a fractional part of another fractional part. First, ask students to consider a coin or sets of coins as part of a dollar. For example, a quarter is 1/4 of a dollar and $.30 is 3/10 of a dollar. Have students find the following amounts:

3 quarters [3 × 1/4 = 3/4 of a dollar; $.75]
5 quarters [5 × 1/4 = 5/4 = 1 1/4 of a dollar; $1.25]
8 dimes [8 × 1/10 = 8/10 of a dollar; $.80]
1/5 of a quarter [1/5 of 1/4 = 1/5 of $.25 = $.25 ÷ 5 = $.05, or a nickel, which is 1/20 of a dollar; 1/4 × 1/5 = 1/20]

Activity 1
Multiplying Fractions by Whole Numbers. Distribute page 118 and *Rainbow Fraction Tiles*. Display the transparency of page 118 on the projector. Write 3 × 1/4 in the fraction boxes and ask students how they would show this problem with the tiles and what the product would be [three 1/4-tiles = 3/4]. Give students other problems such as: 4 × 2/12 and 5 × 1/3.

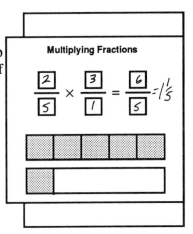

Activity 2
Multiplying Fractions by Fractions. Show a 1/2-tile on page 118. Then ask what 1/2 of 1/2 is and have students find a tile for the answer [1/2 of 1/2 = 1/4]. Next, write 1/3 × 3/4 and ask students for a solution [1/3 × 3/4 = 1/4].

1/2 × 4/5 [2/5]   1/6 of 6/12 [1/12]   2/3 × 9/10 [3/5]
3/4 of 4/6 [1/2]   1/2 × 1 1/2 [3/4]   2/5 of 1 5/10 [3/5]

Practice
Try some of these with students:
1/2 × 8/12 [1/3]   1/4 × 4/6 [1/6]   2/3 × 6/6 [2/3]
3/4 × 1 1/3 [1]   1/2 × 1 3/5 [4/5]   2/3 × 1 1/8 [3/4]

Wrap-Up
Have students demonstrate the solutions to the problems on the projector.

Extension Activity
Challenge students with some of these problems:
1/2 × 3/4 [3/8]   3/4 × 1/2 [3/8]   2 × 1 3/5 [3 1/5]

Overhead Manipulatives in Action, 3–6
© 1992 Learning Resources, Inc.

Rainbow Fraction Tiles

Multiplying Fractions

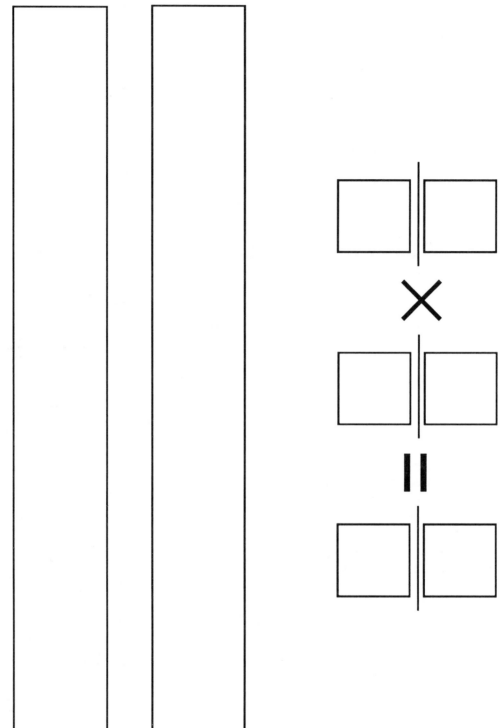

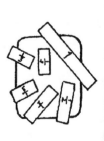

Overhead Manipulatives in Action, 3–6
© 1992 Learning Resources, Inc.

Dividing Fractions

✔ Objective

To divide with fractions.

Vocabulary

divide, quotient, dividend

Materials

Overhead Rainbow Fraction Tiles, transparency of page 120, blank transparencies, overhead pens; *Rainbow Fraction Tiles*, student copies of page 120, pencils

Warm-Up

Write the following problems on the projector one at a time. Discuss what each problem means and what the relationship of the quotient is to the dividend and the divisor.

7) 35 [5]   20) 35 [more than 1; 1r15 or 1.75]
35) 35 [1]   40) 35 [less than 1; 0.875]
70) 35 [1/2 or 0.5]   1/2) 35 [70]
1/2) 1 [2]   1/2) 3/4 [more than 1, less than 2]

When dividing one number (dividend) by another number (divisor), the problem is asking how many of one number (divisor) is contained in the other number (dividend). For 20) 35, ask **How many 20s are in 35?** [1 and something left over] For 1/2) 35, ask **How many halves are in 35?** [70: think of how many half dollars there are in $35.]

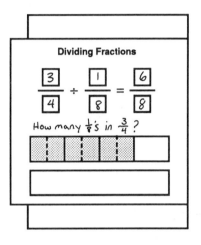

Activity

Dividing Fractions. Distribute page 120 and *Rainbow Fraction Tiles*. Display the transparency of page 120 on the projector and write the problem 3/4 ÷ 1/4 in the fraction boxes. Ask students what the problem means. [How many 1/4's in 3/4?] Then write 1/4) 3/4 and 3/4) 1/4 and ask students which problem is the same as 3/4 ÷ 1/4. [1/4) 3/4] Show 3/4 (three 1/4's) on one of the strips under the problem and demonstrate how there are 3 1/4's in 3/4.

Then try these problems with students:

3/4 ÷ 1/8 [6]   3/4 ÷ 3/8 [2]   3/4 ÷ 3/4 [1]   3/4 ÷ 1/2 [3/2 or 1 1/2]

Next try a problem such as 1/2 ÷ 5/6. Ask students to estimate whether the solution is less than 1 or greater than 1. [Less than 1; divisor is greater than dividend. The solution is 3/5.] Remember: When the divisor is less than the dividend, the quotient is greater than 1. When the divisor equals the dividend, the quotient is 1. When the divisor is greater than the dividend, the quotient is less than one.

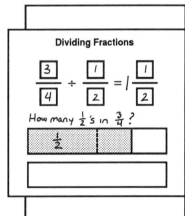

Practice

Have students try some of these:

1/2 ÷ 1/6 [3]   1/2 ÷ 3/12 [2]   2/3 ÷ 1/6 [4]   1/4 ÷ 1/2 [1/2]
4/5 ÷ 1/10 [8]   1 1/2 ÷ 1/4 [6]   3/8 ÷ 1 [3/8]   8/12 ÷ 2/6 [2]

Wrap-Up

Ask students to discuss their solutions with the class.

Dividing Fractions

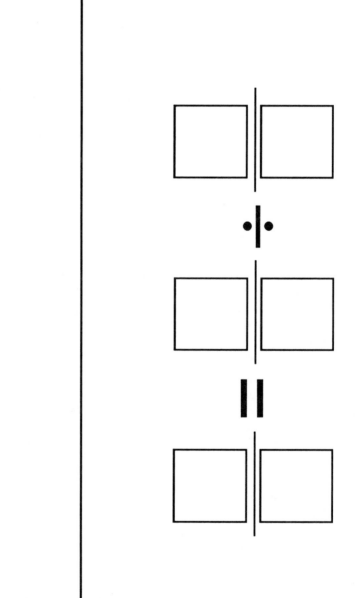

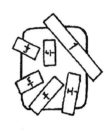

Overhead Manipulatives in Action, 3–6
© 1992 Learning Resources, Inc.

Student Progress Chart

Name _____
Grade _____ Year _____
School _____
Teacher _____

Content	Comments	Content	Comments
Base Ten Blocks		**Geoboards**	
Blocks and Numbers		Shapes, Sides, Corners	
Understanding Addition		Stretches and Shrinks	
Understanding Subtraction		Slides, Turns, Flips	
Understanding Multiplication		Exploring Perimeter	
Understanding Division		Exploring Area	
Hundred Board		**Fraction Squares**	
Counting and Order		Fraction Names	
High and Low		Comparing Fractions	
Quick Sums and Differences		Adding Fractions	
Prime Numbers		Fractions and Decimals	
Fractions, Decimals, Percent		Fractions and Percent	
Bills and Coins		**Tangrams**	
Counting Money		Tangram Shapes	
Going Shopping		Making Other Shapes	
Making Change		Exploring Area	
Bunches of Money		Exploring Perimeter	
Divvy It Up!		Tangram Fractions	
Pattern Blocks		**Rainbow Fraction Tiles**	
Ways to Make Yellow		Comparing Fractions	
Finding Fractions		Adding Fractions	
Exploring Symmetry		Subtracting Fractions	
Slides, Turns, Flips		Multiplying Fractions	
Analyzing Angles		Dividing Fractions	

Dear Family,

Your child _____ *is*

learning about _____ *this week*

in school. Here is an activity that can help your child learn more about the concept.

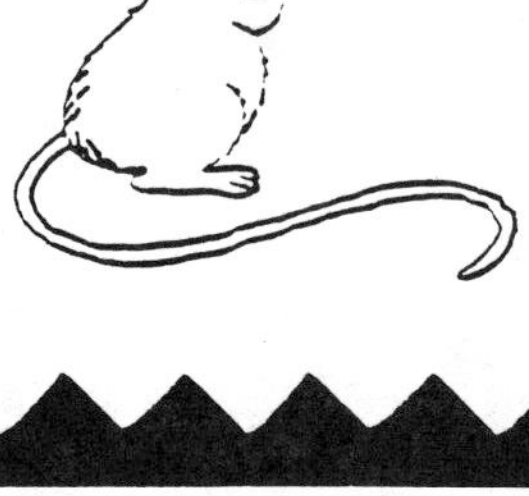

_____

_____

_____

_____

_____

_____

_____

_____

_____

_____

_____

_____

_____

_____

_____

_____

_____

_____

_____   _____

Date   Teacher

Dear _____,

_____

_____

_____

_____

_____

_____   _____
Date   Teacher

GOOD WORK!

▼ ▼ ▼

TO _____

FOR _____

_____   _____
Date   **Teacher**

123

Learning Math

▼ ▼
▼ ▼
▼ ▼

AWARD

TO

_____

FOR

_____

Date _____

Teacher _____